DR. CAROL'S NATURALLY HEALTHY CATS

Carol Osborne, D.V.M.

NEW BURLINGTON BOOKS

A New Burlington Book
Conceived, edited, and designed by
Marshall Editions
The Old Brewery, 6 Blundell Street
London, N7 9BH, U.K.
www.quarto.com

Originated in Singapore by Pica
Cover originated in Hong Kong
by Modern Age
Printed and bound in China by Excel

Library of Congress Cataloging-in-Publication
Data available upon request

ISBN 1-84566-080-3

10 9 8 7 6 5 4 3 2 1

Author Carol Osborne, D.V.M.
Project Editors Elizabeth Tatham, Peter Adams
Art Editor Patrick Carpenter
Managing Art Editor Philip Gilderdale
Managing Editor Antonia Cunningham
Designer Sue Storey
Copy Editor Ben Horslen
Indexer Jill Dormon
Picture Research Antonella Mauro
Editorial Director Ellen Dupont
Art Director Dave Goodman
Editorial Coordinator Ros Highstead
Production Amanda Mackie

Note

Every effort has been taken to ensure that all
information in this book is correct and compatible
with national standards generally accepted at the
time of publication. This book expresses the
opinions of Dr. Carol Osborne and is not intended
to replace consultation with your veterinarian or
complementary therapy practitioner. The author
and publisher disclaim any liability, loss, injury, or
damage incurred as a consequence, directly or
indirectly, of the use and application of the
contents of this book.

For bulk purchases and special sales,
please contact:

American Pet Institute
Attention: Publishing Division
1-866-372-2765

Visit our website:
www.drcarol.com

CONTENTS

Systemic Illnesses

Behavioral Problems

First Aid

INTRODUCTION

As veterinary science and understanding of bodily function improves, our pets are able to live longer and healthier lives. Cats now often live into their twenties because of better sanitation and treatment of infectious disease. You can help your cat enjoy this longer life by paying attention to his nutrition and his general state of health and enabling your vet to act right from the start of any illness. This factfile tells you how to care for your cat, how to recognize when he needs veterinary treatment, and how to care for him at home when he is ill.

No one form of medicine has all the answers. We now realize that stress and anxiety can affect our pets as much as they do ourselves. Parallel with improvements in veterinary science has been a growth in complementary medicine whose qualified practitioners offer a range of treatments for pets. This book tells you about complementary treatments, notably herbal remedies and homeopathy. These treatments will often help to alleviate the symptoms of illness and make your pet feel more comfortable, but they are not a substitute for veterinary advice. If you are worried about your cat's health, you should always contact your vet. The sooner you seek advice, the quicker your cat will feel better.

USING THE FACTFILE

The book is divided into six chapters: 1 The Head; 2 The Digestive System; 3 Skin and Hair; 4 Systemic Illnesses; 5 Behavioral Problems; 6 First Aid. If you know which subject you wish to look up, then simply turn to the relevant tab on the color-coded dividers. On each divider, you will find a table of contents for that part of the book. If you are unsure where to find the information you need, turn to the alphabetical index on page 112.

TEXT AND ILLUSTRATIONS

The text for each ailment is clearly divided into a description of the problem, its causes, and what you or your vet might do to treat it. How you can help your pet, not only during his illness but also by improving his lifestyle so that he is less susceptible to illness in the first place, is also discussed. Anatomical drawings as well as photographs amplify and complement the text.

The book is not intended to be used instead of advice from your veterinarian, but to encourage greater understanding of natural health.

CHOOSING A VET

When deciding on a veterinarian, your initial reaction is generally your best guide. You need to find a person with whom you feel confident and comfortable and who is also conveniently located. It is advisable to register with a vet soon after acquiring your cat so that she can receive a health check and vaccinations can be discussed.

First check the vet's credentials, ask for references, and pay the practice a visit. Find out the opening hours—they may be important if you are working. Make sure that the vet can offer all the services you may need: boarding, grooming, hospitalization, and 24-hour emergency care. Although you may prefer that your cat always sees the same vet, layer group practices usually offer specialization in a variety of areas, which may include alternative medicine. There will also be a greater number of vets available for consultation, which you may consider an advantage. A list of complementary veterinary medical associations that can refer you to qualified practitioners can be found on page 111. Useful website addresses are also provided.

HOW DO I GET THE BEST FROM MY VET?

When you need to consult a vet, it is often easy to overlook matters of concern, so it is a good idea to jot down a few notes to take with you. These should cover topics such as:

• Your cat's origins, age, and history.

• The signs of illness.

• When symptoms first appeared, and whether your cat has suffered from anything similar in the past.

• Any medications your cat is currently taking.

HOLISTIC MEDICINE

Research has shown that health is influenced by physical, mental and emotional factors. Holistic medicine, also known as alternative medicine, aims to take all these factors into account. Herbalism, homeopathy, acupuncture, chiropractic, flower essences and naturopathy are all elements of holistic medicine available for pets. These therapies are not meant to replace conventional veterinary medicine but are used with it to give your cat the best of both worlds.

HERBALISM

Herbalism is probably the oldest form of medicine. Herbal immune therapy is used to stimulate the immune system to fight disease. You should always consult an experienced practitioner since, wrongly used, herbs can produce unwanted side effects. As a general rule, home-grown or bought fresh herbs should be used. To disguise the taste, you should chop them up and mix them into your cat's food, or they can be made into infusions, dips, and tonics.

HOMEOPATHIC REMEDIES

Homeopaths believe that administering an extremely dilute form of a substance similar to the one causing the symptoms stimulates the body to overcome the illness itself. The remedies used are all natural substances and are derived from plants, minerals, or animal products. They are carefully diluted to specific strengths and can be bought in the recommended dilution to be given according to specific guidelines. For cats, they can be given as pellets or crushed to powder and mixed with milk. The cat should not eat any food 10 minutes before or after taking the remedy.

USE WITH CARE

Although complementary remedies are generally safe, they should be used carefully. Seek veterinary advice before giving any medication to your cat, to ensure that her condition has been diagnosed correctly and that the best course of treatment has been chosen. Some common herbs, for example, can have cross-reactions or side effects that you may not be aware of. Also, homeopathic remedies should not be used with acupuncture or strong herbal tinctures. For the best result, work as a team with your vet and complementary practitioner.

OTHER TREATMENTS

Anumber of complementary approaches are useful with cats. You should always seek treatment from skilled practitioners in the field of holistic veterinary medicine.

FLOWER ESSENCES

Flower essences are diluted flower preparations that are used to treat behavioral problems, fears, and other psychological disturbances, especially those associated with stress. They help to rebalance mental and emotional well-being. Originally, Edward Bach, a British physician, developed 38 different flower essences in the 1930s, each of which addressed a specific emotional situation. Today they are known as Bach Flower Remedies. Rescue Remedy is one of the most popular. A mixture of five flower essences, it is commonly used after a phyiscal or emotional trauma or during a stressful situation. For example, for a cat stressed by a major change in his home life, place three drops in his mouth or on his tongue two to three times daily. You can also put the drops into his water bowl. This will help most cats to relax and adjust more easily to the change.

ACUPUNCTURE

Acupuncture is the insertion of needles into specific body points to stimulate the body's immune system to heal itself. It is used to help cats with hip dysplasia, arthritis, bowel diseases with intractible vomiting and diarrhea, and epilepsy. The relief is generally temporary and several treatments are often needed for positive results.

CHIROPRACTIC

Chiropractic is the manipulation of the spinal cord to adjust misplaced vertebrae that may be impinging on nerves and impeding movement. It can be useful to relieve musculoskeletal pain resulting from trauma, arthritis and other degenerative processes affecting the spine and bony skeleton.

NATUROPATHY

Naturopaths believe illness is caused by a buildup of toxins in the body due to poor nutrition and lack of exercise. They recommend a regime of good nutrition and exercise combined with bathing, massage, and sunshine.

GLANDULAR THERAPY

These are biologically active nutritional supplements given as treats or mixed with food. Many contain hormonal material from glands, e.g. the thyroid gland, and are used to stimulate a weakened gland to function normally. When used correctly there are no side effects.

1

THE HEAD

Careful observation of a cat's head can give a good general indication of his overall health status and temperament. First of all, the eyes should be clear and bright, and free of tears. The nostrils should be clean. Runny eyes, a nasal discharge, and sneezing, may indicate a respiratory problem. Ears should smell and look clean, and should not be filled with debris or be scarred. Pearly white teeth with pink gums and fresh breath indicate good, dental health, and the lip margins should be smooth and free of lesions and ulcers. A cat's fur, if healthy, will shine, and should not be matted or soiled; nor should there be areas without hair or that look dry and flaky. Skin parasites like fleas should not be present.

VACCINES

Vaccines help to protect cats against many potentially fatal diseases. Newborn kittens receive natural protection from antibodies in their mother's first milk (called colostrum) while nursing, which lasts for the first few months of life. After that, they have to fend for themselves. Most kittens need a series of shots at 8, 12, and 16 weeks of age, followed by a booster at 1 to 3 year intervals for ongoing protection.

Vaccines are routinely recommended for upper respiratory disease (cat flu), which is caused by feline herpes virus type 1 and feline calici virus, as well as for feline distemper. These vaccines are 80 percent effective. Nasal vaccines, which are squirted up the nose, have recently become available for herpes and calici virus, and some people feel that these provide better protection than injectable vaccines. Side effects of nasal vaccines are mild, and may include sneezing for a few days.

FELINE DISTEMPER VACCINE

Feline distemper, also called feline panleukopenia, is a highly contagious fatal viral disease in cats. The virus attacks the digestive system, and signs include a sudden onset of depression, vomiting, diarrhea, dehydration, and in most cases, death. Vaccination is recommended for all cats.

RABIES VACCINE

Feline rabies is on the increase. At present the number of documented cases exceeds that of all other domestic animals. The disease is a major public health concern. Because of the fatal outcome and potential for human exposure, vaccination is recommended, and is required in many states.

CANCER RISK

Have your vet show you where the vaccination was given. Many cats develop small lumps at injection sites, but most go away on their own. A small number of cats develop a form of cancer called a vaccine site sarcoma, 3 months to 3 years after vaccination. If a lump lasts 6 weeks, have it checked by a specialist. Surgical removal at 6 weeks is a minor procedure; by 12 weeks, it becomes major.

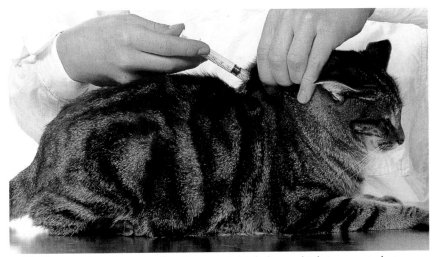

Cats of 12 weeks of age can be given an initial shot, which is repeated at one- or three-year intervals, depending on the vaccine.

FELINE LEUKEMIA VIRUS (FELV) VACCINE

Feline leukemia virus (FELV) is the leading killer of cats today. A vaccine is available, but is ineffective in cats already infected, so cats should be tested first. The vaccine requires two initial doses three to four weeks apart, with annual boosters, and can be given to kittens at eight to 12 weeks of age. Owners with cats at high risk of exposure, such as outdoor cats and show cats, should consider vaccination.

FELINE BORDETELLA VACCINE

Feline bordetella bronchiseptica is a contagious bacteria that occasionally causes or complicates upper respiratory infections in cats. Signs usually include sneezing, runny eyes, and a nasal discharge. A fever and pneumonia may develop. A nasal vaccine is available for cats more than four weeks old.

COMPLEMENTARY TREATMENTS

Homeopathic vaccines are called nosodes. Like vaccines, they stimulate the immune system to protect the cat against infection. Nosodes are made from agents or substances that cause disease. They are sterilized, diluted, and prepared so that they are safe and effective. Nosodes are given by mouth over a period of time that may extend from weeks to months. Nosodes are available for feline distemper, feline leukemia, and feline infectious peritonitis. There is no nosode for rabies.

EYE PROBLEMS

A cat's eyes should normally be clear and bright, and free of any discharge. The leading cause of eye disease in cats is conjunctivitis, which is an inflammation of the membranes lining the eyelids. It leads to red, swollen, itchy, watery eyes. Corneal ulcers, which are abrasions or defects of the cornea (the clear front part of the eye), are very common in cats. Being able to recognize the signs of problems or injury is the best way to prevent permanent eye damage and ensure visual integrity.

CAUSES OF CONJUNCTIVITIS

• Upper respiratory viral infections are a major cause of conjunctivitis (see page 14). Herpes and calici virus may remain dormant in the cat's body and be activated when the cat is sick or stressed, causing the conjunctivitis to recur. Chronic or recurrent bouts of conjunctivitis can lead to a condition called "dry eye."

• An inherited eyelid or eyelash disorder can irritate the eye and causes conjunctivitis. Long-haired Persian cats seem especially prone. Trichiasis is hereditary in this breed.

WHAT YOU AND YOUR VET CAN DO

• A Polymerase Chain Reaction (PCR) is the best and most accurate test available to detect the exact virus responsible. The eye tissue is gently scraped and then sent to the lab.

• Antiviral eye medications include Idoxuridine, Trifluridine, or Vidarabine.

• Cats that do not respond to standard conjunctivitis treatments should be blood-tested for feline leukemia and feline immunodeficiency virus.

SIGNS

Conjunctivitis
• Eyes that are red, puffy, runny, or itchy, or have a mucusy, watery, or yellow-green discharge.
• Pawing and/or rubbing eyes.

Corneal ulcers
• Squinting, watering, or tearing.
• Red, puffy eyes.

Purebreds like this Persian are prone to conjunctivitis.

CAUSES OF CORNEAL ULCERS

• Repeated conjunctivitis due to the herpes virus can cause a condition called "dry eye," which often results in ulcers.

• Hereditary disorders in Persians and Himalayans can cause ulcers.

• Eosinophilic keratitis, an immune system defect, can result in ulcers.

• Chronic irritation from long facial hairs can cause conjunctivitis and, if left untreated, corneal ulcers.

WHAT YOUR VET CAN DO

• Diagnosis is confirmed by staining the eye with a dye that causes the ulcerated or abraded corneal tissue to turn a greenish color. T

COMPLEMENTARY TREATMENTS

For conjunctivitis and corneal ulcers the goal is to reduce further damage and irritation to the eye.

The herb Euphrasia is available commercially as eye drops called "Eyebright." Use 2–3 drops 3 times daily or mix one tablespoon herb, ¼ teaspoon sea salt, and 1 cup of water, bring to a boil, steep, strain, and cool (keeping the liquid sterile.) Use the tea as a compress and apply it over the eye. The astringent Tannin in the herb reduces eye irritation.

Make an eyebright rinse for conjunctivitis.

CAT FLU

Cat flu, also known as feline upper respiratory disease, is a complex illness commonly caused by a combination of viral and bacterial infections. Feline herpes virus type 1 (FHV-1), feline calici virus (FCV), and chlamydia psittaci (a bacteria-like organism) are most often responsible. All cats are susceptible, but kittens with immature immune systems and breeds with facial flattening, like Persians, are more prone.

Once cats are infected, flulike signs develop within a few days. Mild cases usually clear up, with or without treatment, in one or two weeks, but up to 80 percent of cats with herpes and calici virus that apparently recover become carriers. When these cats later become sick or stressed, they shed the virus and act as a major source of infection for the cat community. Many also experience periodic relapses themselves. Cats with chronic herpes virus suffer persistent and recurrent nasal and eye problems, sometimes with high fever and appetite loss. Conjunctivitis and corneal ulcers are the most common eye problems in these cats. Chronic carriers of calici virus may develop severe infections and ulcers of their mouth and gums.

SYMPTOMS

Feline herpes virus (FHV-1)
- Red, runny eyes and squinting (conjunctivitis)
- Runny nose and sneezing; loss of voice

Warning

Respiratory infections are easily spread from one cat to another by sneezing, as droplets travel through the air. Always keep a sick cat indoors to prevent the infection from spreading.

CAUSES

• Ninety percent of feline upper respiratory disease is caused by two viruses: feline herpes virus type 1 (FHV-1), formerly called feline viral rhinotracheitis (FVR), and feline calici virus (FCV). One or more viruses can be present at once; bacteria often complicate the infection.

COMPLEMENTARY TREATMENTS

🖾 DIETARY REMEDIES
Pureé and warm (to room temperature), a mixture of: 1 tsp raw liver, 1 tsp lamb or chicken baby food, 1 tsp cottage cheese, 1 tsp brewer's yeast, and 1 tsp tuna juice (to enhance the smell).

• Herpes virus usually spreads quickly between cats, via sneezing, coughing, grooming, as well as by contact with contaminated items, such as food bowls and bedding.

• Cats are infected with feline calici virus by inhaling or swallowing the virus. The virus can survive for up to 10 days on contaminated items like food bowls. Signs of illness are generally apparent a week after exposure, and cats are usually sick for between one and four weeks. Kittens are affected more severely, and may occasionally die.

WHAT YOU AND YOUR VET CAN DO

• Diagnosis of the type of virus can be confirmed with a test called a polymerase chain reaction (PCR).

• Your vet may prescribe antibiotics, to prevent secondary bacterial problems including pneumonia, topical eye ointments, and nasal decongestants.

• Because there is no cure for a viral infection, therapy consists of good supportive care. Fluids should be administered to maintain hydration, and forced oral feeding may be necessary if the cat refuses to eat. Cats with viral infections often lose their sense of smell, which causes a loss of interest in food, so good nutrition is essential. Soft food with a strong odor helps to stimulate the appetite (see Complementary Treatments, p. 14).

• Clear discharges from the eyes, nose, and mouth with cotton balls soaked in warm water. Vaporize with ½ tsp Vicks Vapo chest rub or 3 drops eucalyptus oil twice daily for 30 minutes to relieve congestion.

• Keep your cat warm and well rested.

SYMPTOMS

Feline calici virus
• Red, runny eyes.
• Sneezing.
• Ulcers on the tongue.

Warning

Contact your vet if your cat has trouble breathing; is refusing to eat or drink; has a fever over 104°F (40°C); or eyes that are partially closed or discharging.

COMPLEMENTARY TREATMENTS

DIETARY REMEDIES

The following remedies are geared to suppress both the herpes and calici virus, and to stimulate the body's natural defenses.

L-Lysine interferes with herpes virus replication. Give 250–500 mg tablets daily, crumbled and mixed into food , or broken up and given piece by piece.

Interferon is an antiviral medication. This should be prescribed and mixed by your vet, frozen, then thawed and squirted into the mouth. Use with Lysine.

Vitamins A, C and E stimulate the immune system.

EAR PROBLEMS

The inside lining of a healthy ear is normally smooth with a small amount of wax buildup. Many problems can cause the ears to be irritated, inflamed and/or infected. Any of these causes left untreated can lead to more complicated problems, including middle- and inner-ear damage, vestibular disease, hematomas, and hearing loss. Most cats let you know that their ears are uncomfortable by scratching, shaking, or tilting their heads.

CAUSES

• Ear mites are the most common ear problems in cats. These microscopic mites irritate the ears and cause itching and a dark brown coffeelike residue. Mites live primarily in the ear canal, but can also live outside of the ear and on other parts of the cat's body. They will not infest your home, but are contagious, and can be spread to other pets and people.

• Small numbers of yeast normally live in the ear canal. Large numbers cause a smelly, waxy buildup.

• Bacteria often occur secondary to inflammation from any cause, including mites and yeast. Bacterial ear infections generally result in a painful, smelly pus-type discharge.

• Trauma to the ear from over-aggressive cleaning can also cause inflammation of the ears.

• Allergic reactions to pollen, mold, plants, and fleas can cause problems.

• Many white cats with blue eyes are born deaf but now hearing is possible with a cochlear implant. Electrodes are implanted into the portion of the inner ear called the cochlea. These stimulate nerves to transmit sound to the brain.

SYMPTOMS

• Persistent scratching of ears.
• Shaking or tilting of the head.
• Odor and/or discharge from ears.

WHAT YOUR VET CAN DO

• Diagnosis is confirmed by a test in which a sample of the ear discharge is examined under a microscope.

• The most effective treatment will be determined, based on whether mites, yeast, and/or bacteria are found.

• Several medications are available for treating ear mites. Tresaderm comes in ear drop form, and is also antibacterial. Revolution, containing the active ingredient selamectin, is approved for use in cats and dogs. It comes as a liquid, which is applied to the skin every 30 days. The added benefit is that it prevents fleas and heartworm.

WHAT YOU CAN DO

• To prevent ear problems, check your cat's ears regularly. Only use products recommended by your vet to clean your cat's ears, and never clean any deeper than you can see. Ask your vet to show you the safest way to clean your cat's ears.

The otoscope, when illuminated, is designed to allow complete visualization of the ear canal.

COMPLEMENTARY TREATMENTS

✉ HERBAL REMEDIES

I tsp of Calendula in I cup of water, plus half tsp of sea salt can be used as an ear cleaner. Calendula oil can also be used to soothe irritated ears. Use 2 drops once a day and leave in ears.

To kill ear mites:
Yellow dock (*Rumex crispus*), 2 drops once a day every third day for 3 to 4 weeks.

▱ HOMEOPATHIC REMEDIES

Pulsatilla 6c, I pellet daily every third day for 30 days, can be used for painful ears.

Sepia officinalis 30c is beneficial if your cat is scratching his ears excessively. Give 2 whole or 3 crushed pellets twice a day, for 3 days.

Calendula oil can relieve the pain of outer ear infections.

DENTAL PROBLEMS

At least 85 percent of all cats and dogs over two years old have gum disease which, left untreated, is now known to be a leading cause of heart disease. Bacteria from the mouth also increase the risk of liver and kidney disease. Other serious problems include oral cancer, of which the most common type in cats is squamous cell carcinoma. Fortunately, most dental problems are preventable and controllable.

SYMPTOMS
Gum disease
• Bad breath.
• Red, swollen gums.
• Dark, discolored teeth.
• Trouble or reluctance eating. .
• Chewing difficulties or excessive drooling.
• Pawing at the face.

CAUSES

• Breed, genetics, age, diet, and general health all contribute to the prevalence and severity of gum disease. If your cat is having trouble eating, is chewing differently, is reluctant to eat, paws at her face, or drools excessively, the mouth may be the problem.

• Bacteria combines with saliva and food particles to form plaque. Plaque accumulates in the spaces between the teeth and gums, and combines with calcium salts to form tartar (which is also called calculus). The bacteria, plaque, and tartar irritate and inflame the gums, causing gum disease. Gingivitis is the medical term for this condition.

• The true cause of squamous cell carcinoma is unknown, but experts speculate that the meticulous grooming behavior of cats makes them particularly prone. Carcinogens from the environment land on the cat's coat and enter the mouth during grooming. These carcinogens cause the cells lining the mouth to divide uncontrollably, and the result may be a tumor. In this case, the squamous cells of the mouth are affected.

WHAT YOU CAN DO

• Dental checkups annually or every six months in middle-aged and older cats allow early detection of problems, including cancer.

COMPLEMENTARY TREATMENTS

☒ **HERBAL REMEDIES**
Neem (Azadirachtairidica) is an herb that prevents bacteria from adhering to teeth. Mix 3 drops tincture with 4 tablespoons of water. Add ⅛ teaspoon of salt. Use to spray teeth and gums.

Sage

For best results, begin brushing when your cat is a kitten. Brushing each of the four outer surfaces of the upper and lower teeth for thirty seconds at least three times a week will decrease bacteria and plaque formation.

• Use a feline toothbrush, or for kittens try a finger cot that fits onto your index finger. Use toothpaste specially formulated for cats. This comes in chicken malt and liver flavors, and is meant to be swallowed. With finicky animals, try clam or tuna juice initially. Do not use human toothpaste

SYMTOMS

Oral cancer
Once a tumor has been present several months:
• Drooling.
• Lack of appetite.
• A red, raised, swollen area of gum tissue, which may or may not be ulcerated.

WHAT YOUR VET CAN DO

• If your cat has a tumor, your vet will take a biopsy to determine whether or not it is cancerous. This involves taking a tiny piece of tissue and examining it microscopically. Squamous cell carcinoma is cancerous, but usually remains in the mouth, although advanced cases left untreated do spread. Complete surgical removal is usually an effective cure, but may not be possible in advanced cases, where masses have grown to a large size. When removal is incomplete, this type of cancer comes back. Supportive therapy would then include pain management, and appropriate feeding.

COMPLEMENTARY TREATMENTS

⊠ HERBAL REMEDIES
Goldenseal (hydrastis canadensis) mouthwash can be used after dental cleaning. Stir 1 tsp of the powdered root stock into 1 pint of water, bring to a boil, and cool. Swab the gums with a cotton ball once daily.

Myrrh (commiphora molol) is an antibacterial herb. To make an oral rinse, mix 3 drops myrrh tincture with

⅛ tsp salt, and 2 fluid ounces water. Bring to a boil, then cool. Swab gums with a cotton ball once daily.

Soothe gums after cleaning with an infusion of purple coneflower (echinacea angustifolia). Mix 1 tsp of rootstock and 8 fluid ounces water. Simmer for 10 minutes. Cool, then strain. Swab gums with a cotton ball twice daily for about ten days.

DRY EYE

The eyelids protect the cornea, the clear outer part of the eye, and the eye itself from trauma. They also produce and spread tears over the eye. Tears supply the cornea with oxygen and nutrients, keeping it healthy. If no tears are produced, a condition called dry eye, where the eyes burn and sting, can result. Pigmentation, scarring, and ulceration of the cornea, or partial vision loss, may result.

CAUSES

• If the eyes of a newborn kitten open before he is 10–14 days old, tears will not be produced, and dry eye will result.

• Certain breeds, including Persians, have an inherited disorder called lagophthalmos. The eyelids do not close properly, so cannot spread tears adequately. Many of these breeds also have mild entropion of the lower eyelid, where the eyelid tissue turns inward and causes further irritation to the eye.

• Chronic herpes virus eye infections can result in dry eye.

WHAT YOU AND YOUR VET CAN DO

• For kittens, topical eye lubricants can be applied until tear production begins. The drug Pilocarpine or the anticancer drug Interferon may stimulate tear production in older cats.

• Surgery may be necessary for cases that do not respond to medication.

COMPLEMENTARY TREATMENTS

⊠ HERBAL REMEDIES
Cod liver oil lubricates dry eye. Apply one drop onto eye every 4 hours. It also contains Vitamin A, which stimulates the body to heal.

▭ DIETARY REMEDIES
Vitamins stimulate healing and boost a cat's natural defenses: Give vitamin E in the form of one 400 IU (International Unit) capsule, broken open and mixed into meals once a week.

MOUTH ULCERS

Oral ulcers, also called canker sores, are lesions that can develop in a cat's mouth. This condition may develop as a result of a reaction to severe untreated gum disease. Destruction of gum tissue may affect the junction where the tooth meets the gum line. In severe cases, affected teeth must be removed to provide a permanent cure.

CAUSES

• Allergic reactions to plaque around teeth, viral diseases such as cat flu, and feline immunodeficiency can all cause mouth ulcers.

• Stress may predispose certain purebreds, including Abyssinians, Persians, Himalayans, Burmese, and Somali.

• Chronic kidney disease can cause ulcers from toxins in the blood.

• Potpourri oil, if ingested, causes mouth ulcers.

WHAT YOU AND YOUR VET CAN DO

• An oral examination of the cat's mouth reveals the ulcers.

• Blood and urine tests rule out problems like kidney diseases that cause ulcers.

• Specific viral tests can detect the calici virus.

• A biopsy of gum tissue detects immune disorders and cancer.

• Initially, therapy involves treating the primary cause, cleaning the cat's teeth, and using oral rinses.

SYMPTOMS

• Red, swollen, severely irritated gum tissue surrounding teeth.
• Ulcers of the gums, tongue, lips, or roof of mouth are also often present.
• Bad breath.
• Difficulty chewing hard food, and may eat only soft food.
• Decreased appetite.
• Weight loss may occur.
• Excess salivation.

COMPLEMENTARY TREATMENTS

⌧ HOMEOPATHIC REMEDIES
Kali bichromicum 200c may be given three times a week, for up to six weeks.

Natrum muriaticum is also used for oral problems including gingivitis, mouth ulcers, and bad breath.

Potassium dichromate, the source of *kali bichromicum.*

FELINE ASTHMA

Feline asthma is a chronic respiratory disease characterized by sudden episodes of breathing difficulty. Episodes can be triggered by allergies and/or stress, both of which cause constriction of the airways. This leads to breathing difficulty, coughing, and wheezing. A low-grade, chronic cough may be the only sign of asthma in a cat, but an acute crisis could occur at any time, and is potentially life-threatening. Affected cats are usually between two and eight years of age. Siamese breeds and females may be more susceptible.

CAUSES

• Allergies to inhaled substances (allergens) in the environment, for example, pollen, mold, dust, kitty litter, powdered carpet cleaner, and tobacco smoke.

• Stress, perhaps as a result of a new pet moving into the home.

• Lung parasites, for example heartworm disease.

• Complications resulting from bacterial infections can damage the airways and result in pneumonia.

SYMPTOMS

• Coughing (similar to hairball cough, but often with difficulty breathing).
• Wheezing.
• Sudden attacks of impaired breathing.
• Breathing may be slow and deliberate or fast and shallow.
• Breathing with mouth open.

THE RESPIRATORY SYSTEM

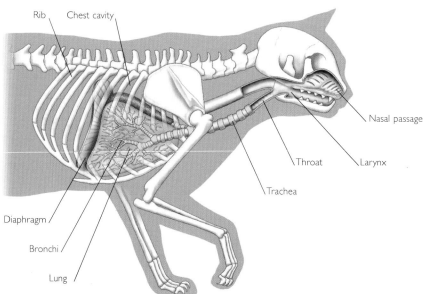

Rib
Chest cavity
Nasal passage
Throat
Larynx
Trachea
Diaphragm
Bronchi
Lung

WHAT YOU AND YOUR VET CAN DO

• The vet will confirm their diagnosis with chest X rays and eliminate other diseases with similar presenting signs, such as bronchitis, heartworm disease, and pneumonia. Fluid and mucus samples may be collected from the airway and examined to pinpoint the exact cause.

• True asthma usually responds quickly to a combination of medications geared to open the airway and block the allergic reaction. Severe cases often also require oxygen therapy. Antibiotics are indicated if bacterial infections such as pneumonia are present.

• Identify and alleviate the causes of stress. Long-term treatment involves removing allergens from the home environment: do not smoke; get an air purifier or an electrostatic air filter; use dust-free, unscented cat litter; and avoid odor-controlling sprays and shag carpeting.

COMPLEMENTARY TREATMENTS

🔲 DIETARY REMEDIES
Vitamins A & E relieve oxidative damage to airways and boost the cat's natural defenses and healing mechanisms.

Vitamin A: Cod liver oil, ¼ teaspoon three times weekly, added to meals. Don't use cod liver oil as a source of fatty acids to avoid excess Vitamin A which can be toxic to cats.
Vitamin E: 400 International Units (IU), break open capsule and mix into meal once a week.

Garlic: Feed ¼ clove of crushed garlic mixed with a dash of Tamari soy sauce. Use 2–3 times a week only because too much garlic can cause anemia in cats.

Garlic is a good natural remedy for chest infections.

CHLAMYDIA

Chlamydia psittaci is a microscopic bacteria-like organism that lives in the white tissue lining of the eyelids ("conjunctiva"). This infection causes a condition called Pneumonitis, and usually affects the respiratory system and/or the eyes. The most common sign is runny eyes due to conjunctivitis (see p. 12). Unlike conjunctivitis caused by cat flu, chlamydial infections usually begin in just one eye, later spreading to involve both eyes. Chlamydia can also cause mild to severe respiratory disease (most infections gradually resolve over 1–2 weeks).

A cat with its haws visible.

WHAT YOU AND YOUR VET CAN DO

• Your vet may prescribe Doxycycline, a type of Tetracycline, which is an effective antibiotic. Tetracycline can permanently stain the teeth of kittens and a different antibiotic is used.

• When chlamydia occurs with the cat flu virus, therapy often includes medications (Interferon and Lysine) to boost the cat's natural defenses and help fight off both bacterial and viral infections.

SYMPTOMS

• Infection that spreads to involve both eyes.
• Tissues lining upper and lower eyelids red, swollen and protruding.
• Thick clear or yellowish discharge.

• Chlamydia is contagious to other cats, and an injectable vaccine is available for prevention, which may be included with the cat flu vaccine. The vaccine will not provide complete protection, but will decrease the severity of the infection. Chlamydial infections can also be spread to people, causing a mild form of the disease known as chlamydiosis, so be sure to wash your hands well after treating your cat.

COMPLEMENTARY TREATMENTS

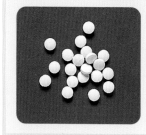

⊠ HERBAL REMEDIES
Apply cold black tea, green tea, or euphrasia tea as a compress over the eyes for a couple of minutes 3 times daily. Apply 2–3 drops Euphrasia or goldenseal eye drops into the eyes three times daily until the conjunctivitis is healed.

Lemna minor tablets help relieve nasal congestion.

THE DIGESTIVE SYSTEM

Because cats clean and groom themselves constantly, vomiting hairballs from time to time is standard for most cats, along with an occasional bout of indigestion. Cats usually gain or lose a few pounds as they age. Their appetite may or may not change accordingly. Most changes occur gradually. They are very subtle and easy to miss. Cats are also experts at hiding signs of illness. Paying close attention to your cat's eating and elimination habits is one of the best ways to detect and help prevent many problems.

A HEALTHY DIET

Proper nutrition is vital to the good health of any cat and maximizes the quality and length of their life. Feeding cats too few or too many dietary nutrients can cause malnutrition and result in potentially serious health problems. In first world countries, overnutrition is a more common problem than undernutrition and 25 percent of our cats are clinically overweight due to being fed diets with excess fat and calories. The composition of commercially available premium foods are regulated by the American Association of Feed Control Officials (AAFCO) and the United States Food and Drug Administration (USFDA) and are a convenient way of providing cats of all ages with a balanced nutritional diet. In general, all cats should eat twice a day. Most cats prefer to "nibble," and this can lead to excess weight gain if their food bowl is not removed between meals. Body weight and physical condition are your best guides on what and how much to feed your cat. Keep snacks to less than five percent of the total diet, and offer healthy treats like carrots, asparagus tips, or a sardine. Variety is also important to help them learn to accept different foods.

TYPES OF FOOD

• Most commercial diets contain substantial amounts of preservatives, artificial coloring, flavoring, and chemicals. The digestible nutritional quality of these foods vary according to the method by which they are processed, i.e. canned, semimoist, or dry. The water content also varies, from approximately 75 percent

DIETARY SUPPLEMENTS

• Salmon oil is the most concentrated form of essential omega 3 fatty acids. Dose: ⅛ teaspoon daily.

• Cod liver oil provides vitamins A and D (do not use as a fatty acid supplement).

• Vitamin B complex is necessary for normal nervous system functions. It combats anxiety and stress. Dose: 10 milligrams daily (¼ of a Multi B tablet).

2

in canned food, to about 10 percent in dry, with semi-moist falling in the midrange. The high water content of canned food helps to prevent feline lower unirary tract disease, since most cats do not adjust their water intake to make up for the difference when they are on a dry food diet. The basic rule is to feed ⅓ cup of dry food daily, or ¼ can of canned food, divided up into two or three meals. The ideal daily amount is provided in a 5.5-ounce can of food.

• Homemade natural diets take more time to prepare, but in many cases are well worth the effort. The key is to balance the ingredients and find a recipe that keeps your cat happy and healthy. A cat's diet should consist of 60–80 percent protein, up to 20 percent vegetables, and up to 20 percent grain.

• Good sources of protein are chicken, lamb, and beef. Liver is a rich source of Vitamin A, which is an antioxident, boosts immunity, and is necessary for cats to digest and absorb protein.

• Vegetable sources include finely grated raw zucchini or carrot; finely chopped alfalfa sprouts; lightly steamed broccoli, carrot, or corn; baked winter squash, yam, or sweet potato.

• Grains that make a useful addition to a cat's diet include soaked oat bran, and cooked barley, millet, oat flakes, brown rice, quinoa, sweet corn, mashed potato, or amaranth.

Canned foods have an average shelf life of one year but spoil quickly once opened.

Dried foods last six months and are convenient and economical, but are less palatable than other foods.

The texture of fresh food will affect its palatibility.

VOMITING

Vomiting is a protective reflex in cats, used to eliminate harmful substances like bones. Occasional vomiting in a healthy cat is generally not a cause for concern. However, vomiting that persists for more than 72 hours, with or without signs of illness such as appetite loss, depression or lethargy, diarrhea, or constipation, can indicate a more severe problem, and should be addressed. The fluids lost during vomiting result in dehydration, which could be life-threatening.

2

SYMPTOMS

- Salivation and hiding prior to vomiting.
- Appearing distressed.

CAUSES

- Hairballs are the most common cause of periodic vomiting.

- Inflammatory bowel disease (IBD) is the most common cause of chronic vomiting (see p. 31).

- Eating linear foreign objects like ribbon, tinsel, or string.

- Round worms in kittens can cause vomiting.

- Many systemic illnesses such as chronic kidney failure cause vomiting. Liver disease can cause vomiting flecked with blood, as can mast cell tumors, a type of stomach cancer in cats.

- Ingestion of poisons, including aspirin, antifreeze, certain plants, pesticides, cleaning agents, lead, herbicides, and heavy metals.

- Distemper virus in unvaccinated cats.

WHAT YOU CAN DO

- Withholding food and water for 6–8 hours allows the body to recover and controls mild cases. Gradually introduce small meals several times daily over the next two to three days.

COMPLEMENTARY TREATMENTS

⬚ HOMEOPATHIC REMEDIES

Nux vomica 6c will help if your cat is moderately ill, or hiding. Give 1 pellet every 4 hours, until signs are gone. Stop if the cat is not better after 24 hours, but continue up to 5 days if he is responding. *Pulsatilla* 6c is good for cats that are reluctant to drink. Use the same dosage as for *Nux vomica*.

✠ HERBAL REMEDIES

Chamomile tea relieves mild cases of nausea and is soothing. Pour 1 cup boiling water over 1 tbsp of the flowers, steep for 15 minutes, drain, and add an equal amount of water. Give 1 tsp at a time, after food and water have already been withheld for the first 6–8 hours.

HAIRBALLS

Grooming is part of a cat's natural behavior. Small amounts of hair are normally swallowed, some of which passes through the digestive tract and is eliminated in the feces. The rest mixes with mucus to form a hairball. Hairballs are dark in color, usually tubular in shape, and mostly made of hair.

Hairballs in the throat area are brought up by regurgitation; those in the stomach are vomited up. The size and number of hairballs produced will depend on the season, the amount of time the cat spends grooming, the cat's health status, and his level of hydration. Most hairballs do not cause serious problems and are more of a nuisance than anything else. Occasionally they become very large, and can obstruct the intestines. This can cause persistent vomiting, with or without constipation. In extreme cases, surgery may be required to remove the hairball.

SYMPTOMS

• Coughing up a tubular mass of hair, or vomiting hair and mucus.

2

NATURAL PREVENTION

• Brush your long-haired cats daily with a wire-bristle brush, followed by a good massage. This is especially stimulating if done just before a meal.

• A variety of foods, treats, laxatives, and lubricants formulated for hairball prevention are available commercially. Give laxatives and lubricants once a week only, as continuous use can interfere with normal digestion and the absorption of food.

• Increase your cat's exercise by providing catnip toys, playing games, or getting another cat.

• Feed edible greens, which are a source of fiber.

COMPLEMENTARY TREATMENTS

□ HOMEOPATHIC REMEDIES
Nux vomica (poison nut) may help the cat to pass the hairball. Give 1 pellet every 4 hours for up to 5 days.

▨ DIETARY REMEDIES
Feeding your cat a natural diet that is high in fiber will help to prevent hairballs and obesity. Fiber sources that can be added to food include ⅛ tsp ground psyllium husks; ⅛ tsp powdered or fine bran; 1 tsp grated carrot 3 times per week; 1 tbsp baby food vegetables; 1 tsp canned pumpkin or strained prunes once a day.

APPETITE LOSS

Cats are naturally finicky when it comes to food, and missing an occasional meal is not unusual. However, cats that stop eating completely, even for a few days, require medical attention, since it could be a sign of illness. They can also develop a liver problem called fatty liver disease or hepatic lipidosis, which is very serious (see p. 70).

CAUSES

• Anything that interferes with a cat's sense of smell, such as a runny nose or nasal congestion, can result in appetite loss. Viral upper respiratory infections, including feline herpes virus and calici virus, are typical examples.

• Fatty liver disease can be caused by not eating. It can also cause continued loss of appetite. Overweight cats are more likely to develop fatty liver disease.

SYMPTOMS

• Loss of interest in food over 2–3 days.

• Overaggressive weight-reduction programs can cause appetite loss.

• Chronic kidney disease.

• Chronic immune diseases, including feline leukemia, feline immunodeficiency virus, feline infectious peritonitis (FIP), and cancer.

WHAT YOU AND YOUR VET CAN DO

• To stimulate your cat's appetite, correct any underlying problems that may be interfering with your cat's sense of smell. A nasal decongestant may help to stimulate the appetite of a cat with a runny nose.

• Foods with a strong odor, for example lightly cooked chicken liver, can be mixed into food to enhance the flavor, which may stimulate the appetite. Canned food is generally preferable to dry food for this. All foods should be warmed to room temperature.

• Petting your cat while hand-feeding may encourage eating.

• Your vet may prescribe an appetite stimulant, or suggest force-feeding by means of a stomach tube as a last resort.

COMPLEMENTARY TREATMENTS

▨ DIETARY REMEDIES
It is sometimes possible to stimulate a cat's appetite with injections of vitamin B_{12}. Feeding a mixture of honey and yogurt may help, as can giving 4 oz (125g) raw liver once a week for life.

IBD

Inflammatory bowel disease (IBD) is the leading cause of chronic vomiting, diarrhea, and weight loss in cats and dogs. Middle-aged and older cats are most prone. It is a chronic condition that affects the function of the stomach and the intestines. Abnormally large numbers of blood cells invade the bowel, which interferes with the digestion and absorption of food. When the cells invade the stomach and initial part of the intestine, vomiting is the main sign. Loose stools and diarrhea develop when the cells invade the lower small intestine. Any or all of the intestinal tract, from the stomach and small intestine to the colon, may be involved. Involvement of the colon results in mucusy diarrhea that is often flecked with bright red blood.

2

SYMPTOMS

• Chronic vomiting, diarrhea, and weight loss.

CAUSES

• The underlying cause of this disease is not known. Immune system defects, food allergies, and stress have been incriminated, but a link has not been confirmed. Infectious peritonitis (FIP) has also been associated with certain cases, but its significance is not known at present.

WHAT YOU AND YOUR VET CAN DO

• A strict allergy-free, hypoallergenic diet (combined with prescribed medication) will help decrease inflammation in the bowel within the first three weeks of therapy. Adding fiber (oat bran) and using protein such as duck or lamb (in allergy-free diets) will support normal intestinal function (motility).

• For IBD, the vet will make routine laboratory tests to check for other causes of chronic vomiting and diarrhea, but these are usually negative. A biopsy (a microscopic examination of tissue samples taken from sites in the bowel) confirms the diagnosis. Medications for reducing inflamation include Flagyl and Prednisone. Azathiopine and Cyclosponne are used in more severe cases.

COMPLEMENTARY TREATMENTS

✕ HERBAL REMEDIES
Slippery elm adds bulk to the stool, which helps to resolve diarrhea. Chamomile reduces bowel inflammation and acts as an antioxidant. Probiotics and fruit sugars rebalance intestinal bacteria necessary for digestion in the colon.

✓ DIETARY REMEDIES
Glucosamine promotes healing of the intestines. Give as a 2% oral solution.
Vitamins A, C, and E act as antioxidants.
1 tsp salmon oil added to meals provides omega 3 fatty acids.

OBESITY

Twenty-five percent of cats are clinically obese, which means that they have more than 15–20 percent body fat. Obesity reduces a cat's lifespan, predisposing him to heart disease, skin disorders, arthritis, fatty liver disease, cancer, lower urinary tract disease, and diabetes. Body weight is influenced by many factors, but over-feeding and too many treats are the most common cause of obesity. Obesity can also cause or result from diabetes. In either case, weight loss will help to regulate blood sugar, and may decrease or eliminate the need for insulin. Obesity also makes anesthesia a more risky procedure, and decreases a cat's stamina and tolerance to heat.

CAUSES

• Overfeeding

• Diabetes

• The aging process. Weight problems in cats increase with age.

• Breed and genetics. Mixed breed cats are more likely to suffer from weight problems than pure breeds.

• Neutering male and female cats decreases their metabolism by 20 to 25 percent, and may therefore result in weight increase. Reducing calories by the same amount will help to prevent this.

• Low levels of thyroid hormone can cause excess weight gain.

SYMPTOMS

• Abdomen is wider than chest.
• Bulge in groin area.

WHAT YOU AND YOUR VET CAN DO

• Determine whether or not your cat is overweight. Most cats should weigh between eight and 13 pounds (3.5–4.5 kilograms) and have an hourglass figure, with the chest wider than the abdomen.

- Before starting your cat on any weight-loss program, take him to a vet so that they can rule out medical problems that mimic obesity, like heart and liver disease, hypothyroidism, and diabetes.

- For your cat to lose weight successfully, you need to reduce his total number of calories and increase his daily exercise. Weigh your cat every 2 weeks using the same scale to monitor his progress. Ultimately, the success of your cat's weight loss program depends on your cat and you.

- For best results, weight loss should occur slowly. Cats should not lose more than 1 or 2 pounds per month. Overaggressive weight reduction programs can lead to appetite loss and fatty liver disease. Use lean, high-quality protein sources like chicken, beef, or liver. At least 35 percent of the diet should be protein.

2

- Reduce dietary fat to less than 10 percent of the diet. This may cause your cat's skin and haircoat to become dry. Fatty acid supplements such as fish oil and flax seed oil will help to prevent dry haircoats.

- Under your vet's guidance, increase fiber in the diet by 15–30 percent. Fiber provides bulk, which will make the cat feel full. Excess fiber, however, can interfere with absorption of minerals, and lead to other nutritional problems.

- Avoid snacks and feed your cat healthy treats like fresh vegetables.

- Provide a good vitamin supplement.

- Feed your cat smaller meals more often. Try increasing the number of meals from one or two, to six. Spread the food out on a large cookie platter, which will make it take longer to eat.

- Leave food out for 30 minutes, then remove.

COMPLEMENTARY TREATMENTS

⊠ HERBAL REMEDIES
Catnip (*Nepeta cataria*) stimulates the nervous system, so cats feel good and want to play. It may be stuffed into toys, rubbed on perches, sprinkled over food, or given as a treat.

Kelp is a source of trace minerals and may stimulate your cat's body to help burn calories and promote weight loss. Use with the advice of your vet.

⊠ DIETARY REMEDIES
The following fiber sources can be added to a cat's meals: 1 tsp wheat bran or 1 tsp finely grated carrot, zucchini, peas, corn, or chopped green beans.

DIARRHEA

Diarrhea is the abnormal, frequent passage of loose or soft stools, and is one of the most common signs of disease of the small intestine in cats and dogs. The underlying cause is usually the abnormal absorption of nutrients in the bowel. This can occur because of a variety of problems including inflammatory bowel disease (IBD), viral and bacterial infections, toxins, and dietary factors.

CAUSES

• Viral infections are the most common cause of diarrhea in cats. These include feline distemper virus, feline leukemia virus, and feline aids.

SYMPTOMS

• Large volumes of stool.
• Loose, watery stools.

• Inflammatory bowel disease is the major cause of chronic diarrhea and vomiting in cats and dogs.

• Dietary factors may also result in diarrhea. Milk intolerance, for example, which is the inability to digest lactose, is extremely common in cats and dogs.

• Roundworms and hookworms can cause diarrhea in kittens.

• Toxic plants that are ingested can cause diarrhea as can insecticides like organophosphates in flea products.

• Human pain relief medications can cause diarrhea or be fatal.

• Bacterial infections such as salmonella are a risk in cats that hunt birds, and can cause diarrhea.

WHAT YOU AND YOUR VET CAN DO

• Diarrhea that lasts 24 hours or less in an otherwise healthy cat can be beneficial, since it cleanses the body, and is not a cause for concern.

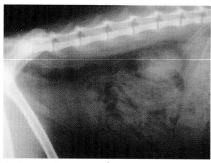

An X ray of your cat's stomach may be necessary to check for foreign bodies.

• Diarrhea lasting more than 24 hours or occurring in a sick cat that is not eating, is depressed, or is vomiting, can cause life-threatening dehydration and requires veterinary intervention.

• Your vet may perform a fecal exam to check for worms, a blood test for viral infections, or take X rays to find out whether foreign objects have been swallowed or tumors are present.

2

WHAT YOU CAN DO

• For simple diarrhea lasting less than 24 hours in an otherwise healthy cat, withhold food for 12–24 hours, but provide fluids to prevent dehydration. Offer your cat chicken broth, which you can make by mixing ½ cup chicken purée with 2 tablespoons of water and 1 teaspoon yogurt. Warm to room temperature. Once the diarrhea has subsided, feed your cat small amounts of bland food like boiled chicken and rice, strained lamb baby food, or uncreamed cottage cheese.

• ½ tsp Kaopectate up to 3 times a day usually helps to stop diarrhea.

• Fiber in the diet adds bulk to stools and helps to solidify the feces. Good sources include psyllium, slippery elm, and vegetables.

• A 2 percent solution of glucosamine, an essential nutrient, in water can be given under your vet's advice.

2

Water is the single most important nutrient for preventing dehydration in a cat suffering from diarrhea.

COMPLEMENTARY TREATMENTS

⬚ HOMEOPATHIC REMEDIES
Natrium muriaticum 6x, I pellet by mouth every 4 hours for 3 treatments. Use for longer-lasting diarrhea, especially if your cat seems uncomfortable, but if he is not better in 24 hours, try another remedy.

✄ HERBAL REMEDIES
Slippery Elm powder is a good treatment for diarrhea. Mix I tsp with I cup cold water, bring to a boil then simmer for 3 minutes. Cool to room temperature and give ½–I tsp every 4 hours by mouth.

▨ DIETARY REMEDIES
Yogurt with live bacteria cultures will help to replace the bacteria lost in diarrhea.

Yogurt

CONSTIPATION

Constipation is the infrequent passage of stool, which may be accompanied by straining to defecate. The feces may be hard, or just firmer than normal. Recurrent constipation can lead to a condition called obstipation, which is severe, persistent constipation. Nerve damage to the colon resulting from repeated bouts of constipation may be the underlying cause. The colon, which is the last or terminal portion of the large intestine, becomes dilated. Stool retained for abnormally long periods of time gets extremely hard, and obstipation may require surgical intervention to bring the cat relief.

CAUSES

• Very large hairballs form masses called trichobezoars, which are a leading cause of constipation in cats. Certain breeds with obsessive behavioral disorders, particularly Siamese, may groom themselves excessively and therefore be more prone to hairballs.

• Dietary indiscretion is unusual in cats, but certain eating disorders involving ingestion of wool and other fibers may cause constipation.

• Chronic kidney failure in older cats results in dehydration and electrolyte imbalances. Dehydration causes the body to absorb more water from the feces, which makes them harder.

• Anal sac problems including abscesses are painful, and cats may be reluctant to defecate as a result.

• Certain medications like antidepressants, diuretics, and anticonvulsants can cause constipation as a side effect.

SYMPTOMS

• Firm stool.
• Straining to defecate.

WHAT YOU AND YOUR VET CAN DO

• If you notice that your cat is only straining or making multiple trips to the litter box and producing no stool or urine, constipation may not be the problem. Your cat may be straining to urinate, which is a true emergency and requires immediate veterinary intervention.

• Mild episodes of constipation in an otherwise healthy cat can often be successfully managed at home.

• The importance of fluids for maintaining hydration is often overlooked. Increase your cat's fluid intake by making a thick broth of chicken, turkey, beef, or liver, adding a few drops of soy sauce for taste.

2

• Increase the amount of fiber in your cat's diet. Fiber is not absorbed and adds bulk to the stool, stimulating the colon to contract and expel the feces. Good sources of fiber include fine bran (⅛ tsp added to each meal), stewed prunes or prune juice (½ tsp added to each meal). Metamucil, Konsil, and Siblin (½ tsp added to meals) are commercially available products.

• Consider changing to a diet with higher fiber levels, up to 10 percent to help prevent recurrences. Talk to your vet first.

• Add ½ tsp melted butter or 1 tsp baby food vegetables to your cat's meals, which will help to soften stools.

COMPLEMENTARY TREATMENTS

✖ HERBAL REMEDIES
Ground psyllium husks (labeled under the name Vetasyl), ⅛ tsp added to meals, will stimulate the intestine to absorb water, which softens and promotes the passage of feces.

▢ HOMEOPATHIC REMEDIES
For obstipation, give your cat one dose of Sepia 30c (2 whole or 3 pellets crushed and placed on tongue). Do not

feed 1 hour before or after treatment.

▨ DIETARY REMEDIES
Vitamin C powder, 250 mg twice daily, or zinc, 5 mg daily, will help to relieve constipation.

FOOD ALLERGIES

Food allergy is an abnormal or hypersensitive reaction to an ingredient in food, which is usually a protein. Ten to 20 percent of allergies in cats are caused by food. Siamese and Siamese crossbred cats under two years old are more prone to food allergies. One third of cats with food allergies also have flea allergies.

CAUSE

• Beef, dairy products, and fish, especially tuna and mackerel, are responsible for almost 90 percent of food allergies in cats. These products cause a skin reaction, as opposed to diarrhea.

• An allergy to milk, which results from lactose intolerance, causes diarrhea.

• Food preservatives like benzoic acid and propylene glycol are toxic to cats and may cause an allergic reaction.

SYMPTOMS

• Severe itching all over the body.
• Itching with small scabs located primarily on the head, neck, and ears.
• Diarrhea.

WHAT YOU CAN DO

• The only way to find the true cause of a food allergy is an elimination diet. A single source of protein is used for 12 weeks and, if the cat's condition improves, other sources are added back into the diet one at a time, every five to seven days, until the reaction recurs. This identifies the problem food.

• Hydrolyzed proteins are conventional proteins broken down to such a small size that they do not cause an allergic reaction. Hypoallergenic diets containing hydrolyzed protein are available commercially.

COMPLEMENTARY TREATMENTS

🔲 HOMEOPATHIC REMEDIES

Vitamin C in high doses acts as an antihistamine and may help if your cat is suffering from itching. A good source of vitamin C is Ascerbate powder; 100 mg 3 times a day is an average dose, but check with your vet to be sure.

SKIN AND HAIR

Skin diseases are very common in cats. They can occur because of bacterial, viral, fungal, allergic, parasitic, and hormonal disorders. In older cats, skin cancer and cysts are not uncommon. Signs of skin problems are among the easiest to detect. They include dry flaky skin as well as red, raw, irritated areas often with hair loss and small scabs. Since the signs for different skin diseases are often similar, diagnosis can be difficult. Unfortunately, many skin diseases are chronic and cannot be cured, but they can be controlled. These cases often require long-term treatment, which is frustrating and costly. Nutrition, bathing, and grooming provide symptomatic relief in almost all cases.

GOOD GROOMING

Regular grooming helps to keep your cat's skin and haircoat in good condition. It decreases hairballs and mats, removes dead skin and hair, and degreases the coat. Grooming is also a good way to reinforce the bond between you and your cat and gives you a chance to check for fleas and ticks, as well as lumps and bumps. How often you groom your cat will vary depending on the hair length and type of coat, and on whether the cat lives mostly inside or outdoors

Slicker brushes are particularly good for removing the dead hair on short-haired cats.

3

GROOMING TIPS

• Short-haired single-coated cats benefit from grooming once a week. Use a metal-toothed slicker brush and groom them in the direction the fur is lying.

• Cats with semilong hair need more regular grooming with a natural-haired brush to keep their coats healthy and mat-free. Your cat's coat condition is your best guide as to how often grooming is needed.

• Long-haired double-coated cats need daily grooming. First brush the fur backward, then brush it forward. Use a wide-

Slicker brush

Wire-bristle brush

Nylon-bristle soft brush

Flea comb

toothed metal comb with a maximum of ten teeth per inch and a brush with natural bristle. Avoid using nylon-bristled brushes because they tend to cause static electricity in the fur, which increases tangles.

• Let damp fur dry before trying to remove twigs, leaves, and other outdoor debris that is caught in your cat's coat.

• Scissors with curved blades work best to snip out any mats.

• Finish combing the cat with a fine-toothed flea comb.

• Kittens should be groomed so that they get used to the procedure. Placing the kitten on a table with a nonslip surface helps him feel secure.

• Curly-coated cats, such as the American Wirehair and the Devon and Cornish Rex, should not be brushed or combed but do need monthly baths.

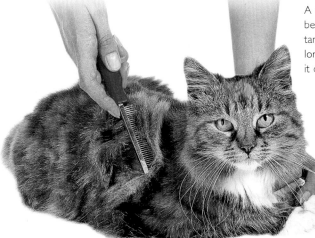

A wide-toothed comb is best for gently removing tangles from the coats of long-haired cats because it doesn't pull the fur.

3

BATHING YOUR CAT

• Prepare everything in advance: use a figure-8 harness attached to a leash that can be fastened to the wall next to your tub or sink with a suction cup. This will secure the cat and leave both your hands free. Place a nonskid rubber mat on the bottom of the tub or sink so that your cat has secure footing. Fill the sink or tub halfway with lukewarm water.

• Before the bath, brush out the coat. This helps to remove mats, which are twice as hard to get out once wet. Lubricate your cat's eyes with artificial tears, or one drop of vitamin E oil, and put a cotton ball in each ear.

• Rinse the coat down gently and shampoo twice; use products that are specifically designed for cats. Massaging your cat's body helps get the suds good and foamy. Then rinse off the fur thoroughly.

• Squeeze out excess water with your hands and towel dry. Do not use towels washed with fabric softeners because they absorb less water and leave a residue on the cat's coat. Remove the cotton balls from your cat's ears.

ITCHING

Itching is the most common sign of allergies in cats. Allergic dermatitis is an inflammation of the skin that occurs after it has been exposed to something to which it is allergic, known as an allergen. Cats lick, bite, chew, and scratch themselves to the point of self-mutilation. The result is red, raw areas of skin with oozing sores and hair loss.

SYMPTOMS

- Scratching.
- Licking and biting.
- Excessive grooming.
- Small scabs on head, neck, and ears, or all over body.
- Hair loss with or without scabs.
- Skin crusts and plaques on head, neck, and back.

CAUSES

- Fleas are a major cause of itching and cause up to 90 percent of skin allergies in cats.

- Inhalent allergies are the second most common type of allergy in cats and a major cause of itching. Outside, these can be triggered by airborne mold, pollen, or grass particles. Indoors, tobacco smoke, carpet cleaners, and perfumes are common causes.

- Most food allergies, except "milk intolerence."

- Parasite infestation, for example ticks, mites, lice, and insect bites.

- Fungal infections such as ringworm, and dry skin.

WHAT YOU OR YOUR VET CAN DO

- Conuslt a vet to diagnose the underlying cause.

- Antihistamines are effective in relieving itching in certain cases Corticosteroids may be the only effective medication.

- Vitamin C with bioflavonoids acts like an antihistamine.

- Oatmeal-based shampoos and Witch Hazel relieve irritation temporarily.

- Eliminate fleas (see p. 44).

Ear mites (see p. 17) can cause cats to scratch their ears.

3

COMPLEMENTARY TREATMENTS

▨ DIETARY REMEDIES
Fish oil, flaxseed evening primrose oil, and salmon oil all help to supplement fatty acids that prevent the skin from drying out.

▨ HERBAL REMEDIES
Aloe Vera gel, available from health food stores, contains enzymes that reduce skin irritation. Apply topically. Comfrey, which contains allantoin, promotes healing and can be used as a rinse. Camomile has antioxidant properties and helps reduce skin irritation and relieve itching. Give one teaspoon of Camomile tea served cold four times a day.
Ready-made herbal tinctures have the same benificial effects. Use one or two drops and serve in a broth to disguise the taste.

▨ HOMEOPATHIC REMEDIES
Graphites 6x, a form of carbon, is recommended when the affected areas are sore, and there is a thick discharge on the skin. Place one pellet on your cat's tongue every 4 hours until signs are gone for up to five days. Withold food 10 minutes before and after treatment. If there is no improvement after 24 hours, discontinue treatment. *Rhus toxicodendron* 6x (poison ivy) should be used in the same way, for a maximum of five days. Stop the treatment earlier if the symptoms are alleviated. This is a more suitable remedy in cases of red, rather than broken, skin, particularly if there is also severe irritation.

More intense itching may respond better to *Arsenicum album* 30c (arsenic trioxide). Dosage as above.

FLEAS

Fleas are skin parasites that bite people and pets and are the most common source of itching and skin irritation in cats. Fleas, which can live up to a year, suck blood and can also cause anemia and transmit tapeworms. They only stay on your pet long enough to get a blood meal, then jump down to lay more eggs. Finding one flea on your cat means thousands more nearby.

SYMPTOMS

- Scratching the head, neck, and ears.
- Flea dirt may be visible.

3

WHAT YOU AND YOUR VET CAN DO

• Signs of fleas include itching, especially on the head and neck, and tiny black specks that look like dirt. To confirm that this "dirt" is caused by fleas, place it on a moist cotton ball. Flea dirt will turn red because of the blood it contains.

• Once a flea problem has been found, you need to treat all of the pets in the home, and the home itself. Vacuum the carpets and upholstery and throw away used vacuum bags so that flea eggs do not hatch in the bag. To protect against flea infestation for up to one year, sprinkle sodium polyborate powder, a "borax," onto the carpet before vacuuming. You can also use Pyripoxifen or Methoprine on carpeting. These are insect growth regulators that works by preventing flea eggs from hatching and last up to 18 months. Be sure to wash your cat's bedding with hot, soapy water. Finally, bathe all the animals living in your home. Use a flea shampoo with pyrethrins or d-limolene as the active ingredient.

• A range of new regulator products are available from vets that protect your cat from fleas for 30 days or more and are safe enough to be used on kittens. Of these, Frontline and Revolution come in liquid form and should be applied at 30-day intervals. Many of them are effective against multiple parasites.

COMPLEMENTARY TREATMENTS

⊠HERBAL REMEDIES
A number of herbs used topically reduce itching and skin irritation. Comfrey contains allantoin, which promotes healing. Chamomile has antioxidant properties.

The best way get rid of fleas in outdoor environments is to spray infested areas with natural products that contain nematodes. These microscopic worms eat the larval and pupal forms of fleas and 250 other outdoor pests.

FLEA BITE ALLERGY

Over 90 percent of skin allergies in cats are caused by flea bites. The allergy is actually a reaction to a protein compound in the fleas' saliva. It generally develops in cats over three years old since their sensitivity to this protein increases with age. When "allergic cats" are bitten by fleas they will lose hair and scratch until the skin is raw. Often this results in secondary bacterial skin infections. Up to one third of cats have multiple allergies. If your cat's scratching has not resolved once fleas have been eliminated, have your cat tested by your vet to see if she is allergic to other insects, such as mosquitoes, or is suffering from either an inhalant or a food allergy.

SYMPTOMS

- Excess scratching on head, neck, and ears.
- Reddened, raw skin.
- Small scabs on head, neck and body.
- Hair loss.

WHAT YOU AND YOUR VET CAN DO

- Today, prevention is the key to flea control. Safe and effective for both cats and dogs, Lufenuron is an injection given every six months that controls fleas and prevents contamination of your home.

3

- Several new products are given as tablets by mouth or as liquids applied to the skin between the shoulder blades at 30-day intervals (see p. 44).

- Diatomaceous earth, which is derived from microscopic algae, can help to kill fleas safely in the home by dehydrating them on contact. Apply this product to the floor (wearing a mask), and focus on the areas like gaps between carpeting and walls or hardwood floors where fleas often lurk. Prevention should start in spring when outdoor temperatures regularly exceed 65°F (18°C).

COMPLEMENTARY TREATMENTS

✉ HERBAL REMEDIES

A lemon juice solution alleviates irritation caused by fleas and other insect bites, as well as skin allergies. To make a solution, cut a lemon into thin slices, boil in one pint of water, and steep for eight hours. Cool and use as a dip or daily spritz.
Another natural herbal itch remedy can be prepared by making tinctures with cats' claw, licorice root, and dandelion. Mix five drops of each tincture, then give three drops of the solution once daily for 14 days. You can give it to the cat by mouth or mix it in his food.

As well as being an anti-inflammatory, lemon also acts as an antihistimine.

TICKS

Ticks are external parasites that suck blood from other animals to survive. They are most prevalent in wooded rural areas but can be found anywhere animals live. Ticks bite a variety of animals, including cats, dogs, livestock, snakes, rodents, birds, and people. Most ticks are just a nuisance, but some transmit disease. For example, certain deer ticks carry Lyme Disease, which is an illness that can affect cats, dogs, and people.

WHAT YOU CAN DO

• Most ticks must be attached to their victim for at least 24 hours to transmit disease. Prompt removal prevents most problems.

• To remove a tick, wear gloves and use a pair of tweezers. Grasp the mouthparts of the tick as close to the skin as you can and pull back gently. If part of the tick's head is left behind, use a sterilized needle to remove it. Do not squeeze the tick because that could cause the contents of the tick's body to be injected into the person or pet and, if the tick is carrying a disease, the individual could become infected.

• Preventing your pet from getting ticks in the first place is also possible through a new, over-the-counter product containing Fipronyl called Frontline. Frontline is applied to the skin at 30-day intervals and kills adult fleas on contact. It has the added benefit of tick control and is safe and approved for kittens over 12 weeks old.

• To be sure that you are at no risk of infection, place ticks removed from the body in a sealed jar with a little alcohol in it. You can call your vet or physician to identify the type of ticks if you are worried that they are a disease-carrying variety.

SYMPTOMS

• Embedded ticks can resemble a wart or a swelling. Closer examination revealsthe legs and the mouthparts.
• Cat will scratch at the area.
• Secondary infections of the skin may develop.
• Lyme Disease affects the skin, joints, and nervous system. In cats, signs are often vague, but include arthritis with fever, lethargy, and appetite loss.
• Treatment of Lyme disease with antibiotics for two to four weeks can be an effective treatment, especially in the early stages, but relapses may occur.

COMPLEMENTARY TREATMENTS

⊠ HERBAL REMEDIES
Calendula made in tea form and used as a compress promotes the healing of skin lesions the tick may have caused.

Calendula comes from marigold flowers.

3

LICE

Lice are tiny, six-legged parasites that feed on blood and can cause anemia if the animal is run down. They are rarely found on healthy domestic cats or kittens, although head lice on schoolchildren are quite common. Lice are visible to the naked eye under a bright light but the tiny white nits—which are the egg cases—may be more visible attached to the hair of the coat. Lice occur only in the cold winter months and do not infest the home.

SYMPTOMS

• Itching.
• White nits in hair.

CAUSES

• Lice are most likely to appear in cats kept in close proximity to each other. It is always worthwhile checking the fur and skin carefully if your cat has come from a rescue home, or has spent some time in a cattery.

WHAT YOU AND YOUR VET CAN DO

3

• Lice cam be detected using a magnifying glass, and the type can be identified by examination under a microscope.

• Grooming can help to control lice, because they die quickly when removed from contact with the cat.

• Most new products that kill fleas, such as Revolution and Frontline, will kill lice (see p.44). A second application is necessary after two weeks or so to destroy lice that may have hatched from eggs after the first treatment.

• Bathe your cat with pyrethrum or d-limolene shampoo once a week for three weeks, leaving the suds on for 10 minutes before rinsing off.

• Your vet may recommend an antihistamine to control the itching, and advise on giving dietary supplements with B vitamins and iron—for example, brewer's yeast or raw liver—to combat possible anemia. A balanced diet, sunshine, and fresh air restore health.

COMPLEMENTARY TREATMENTS

⊠ HERBAL REMEDIES

Chrysanthemums contain pyrethrins, which are effective against fleas and lice. Citrus fruits such as lemons contain d-limolene, which is also effective.

⊡ HOMEOPATHIC REMEDIES

Sulfur 30c can help to lower the risk of reinfection. Give a dose of two whole pellets or three pellets crushed to a powder once every 30 days.

MANGE

There are two types of mange that affect cats. Notoedric mange (also called feline scabies) is caused by a microscopic mite named *notoedres cati*. These mites burrow deeply into the skin and cause intense itching. They are similar to scabies mites in dogs. Cheytiella mites, which cause walking dandruff are large enough to see. They do not burrow into the skin, and may or may not cause itching. Because of their natural grooming habits, cats may remove mites with their tongue before you can find them. Therefore, detecting mites may or may not be easy. Sometimes a fecal check can reveal walking dandruff mites.

A mange mite

SYMPTOMS

Feline Scabies
• Severe itching.
• Red skin with crusts and scales first appear on tips of ears and can spread to the face.

Walking Dandruff
• Carriers can spread the disease to others and appear normal or just have dry skin.
• Itching, with or without dandruff.
• Scabs and hair loss can occur with itching,

WHAT YOUR VET CAN DO

• For both types of mange, looking at infected skin under the microscope often reveals the mites and confirms the diagnosis.

• The best treatment is Selamectin. This is the active ingredient in a monthly flea-control product called Revolution. Selamectin is a liquid, which is applied to the skin between the shoulders at 30-day intervals and is approved in cats. It also controls ear mites, intestinal worms, and prevents heartworms. All dogs and cats in the house should be treated. Routine use of Selamectin also prevents reinfestation by mites.

• Clean your home thoroughly, using a product that eliminates mites. Your vet will advise you of the best products to use.

• Some cats with walking dandruff may have a defective immune system. Vets call this "autoimmune," which means that the cat's body attacks itself for some reason. The cause of this problem is unknown, but it can occur because of underlying viral diseases like feline leukemia, FIV and FIP.

• Blood tests rule out these viral diseases. Stimulating the cat's natural defenses may help them to heal. Antioxidant vitamins along with several herbs and nutrients are often helpful in boosting the immune system.

Warning

Mites are contagious to other cats, dogs, and humans. In people, the mange usually clears up in a few weeks with or without treatment. Wear disposable gloves and wash your hands well to decrease your exposure risk when handling infected pets.

3

A litter of kittens is vulnerable to mange because the mites that cause this condition spread by direct contact.

• Bacteria may invade areas where *notoedres cati* mites are burrowing under the skin. This can lead to serious and even life-threatening secondary infections, which need to be treated with antibiotics.

COMPLEMENTARY TREATMENTS

HOMEOPATHIC REMEDIES

Sulfur 6x: 1 pellet daily for 30 days may relieve symptoms. Withold food 10 minutes before and after treatment.

HERBAL REMEDIES

Soothe the affected areas by washing them each day using a lemon juice solution (see p. 45). This may help to kill some of the mites.

Lavender oil, diluted 1:10 with almond oil, may help to encourage new hair growth in the case of dandruff mites. Apply topically to affected areas until the new hair starts to appear.

Purple coneflower (*Echinacea angustifolia*) can be used for scabies mites. Apply compresses soaked in the infusion topically to the infected skin.

Purple coneflower

RINGWORM

Ringworm is the most common fungal infection of cats and dogs worldwide and prevails in warm, humid climates. The fungus infects the hair and hair follicles. The classic ringworm lesion is a circular patch of skin with no hairs or broken hairs and edges that may be red, scaly, and crusty. In pets, lesions usually occur on the head or face although they may appear on other parts of the body. Ringworm is easily spread to other animals and people by contact with an infected cat, or by contact with shed hair or skin from that cat. Long-haired cats under one year of age living in multicat environments are most at risk. Some cats, known as "healthy carriers," carry and spread the infection but show no signs themselves

Human ringworm lesion

SYMPTOMS

• Carriers may have only dull, dry haircoats.
• Single or multiple circular lesions with crusting and scaling.
• Occasionally, swollen nail beds are a sign.

CAUSES

• Certain types of fungi called Dermatophytes cause ringworm. In cats, 90 percent of cases are caused by *Microsporum canis*.

WHAT YOU OR YOUR VET CAN DO

• Your vet can diagnose that your cat has ringworm by examining infected hairs under ultraviolet light or else skin scrapings under a microscope. Confirmation of this diagnosis is made at a lab by producing a fungal culture from infected samples.

• The best treatment for most cats is a full body dip given once a week until all the pets in the home are cured. Effective dips that kill this fungus include Nolvasan and a 1 percent solution of Chlorox (1 part Chlorox mixed with 99 parts water). Let the dip dry on the cat and do not rinse it off. (See "Bathing your Cat p.41.)

A ringworm lesion is visible above this kitten's right eye.

• The most effective treatment for your home is to throw out what you can and disinfect the rest. To clean floors and food bowls, a Chlorox solution of 1 part Chlorox mixed with 32 parts water works well. 1 part Nolvasan mixed with 3 parts water makes an effective solution to clean your carpets. A good diet along with plenty of sunshine also promotes healing.

3

Warning

It can take three to four months to completely get rid of the ringworm fungus. Dry clean drapes, steam clean carpets, and clean floors and walls with chlorine bleach. Disinfect all heating and cooling vents and change air filters weekly. Vacuum and clean the pet's cage daily. Be sure to wear gloves and wash your hands well to avoid being infected and spreading ringworm to other family members.

COMPLEMENTARY TREATMENTS

⊠ HERBAL REMEDIES

Herbs like reishi and astralagus stimulate the body to heal itself. Antioxident vitamins A (10,000 IU) and E (400 IU) mixed into meals once weekly also stimulate immunity and promote healing.

Goldenseal (*hydrastis canadensis*) can help resolve skin lesions. Stir one generous teaspoon of rootstock into 8 oz of boiling water. Cool and strain, then massage into lesion twice daily.

☐ HOMEOPATHIC REMEDIES

Sulfur 6x, 1 tablet once a day for 30 days, can be used with any of the herbal remedies listed above.

DRY SKIN

Dry skin is common in cats, especially when the weather gets cold and indoor heating is turned up. Dry skin is flaky and often has white scales that resemble dandruff. Diets deficient in essential omega-3 fatty acids and zinc can lead to dry skin, as can bathing your cat with the wrong type of shampoo. It is a good idea to check with your vet to rule out underlying problems that can cause dry skin. These may include fleas, walking dandruff, mange mites, ringworm, and other disorders.

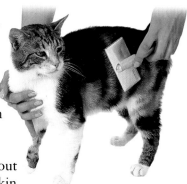

Regular grooming helps to control dry skin.

3

SYMPTOMS

- Dull skin and haircoat.
- White flakes may be visible.
- Itching.
- Fur may feel brittle.
- Excess shedding can occur.

WHAT YOU CAN DO

- Give your cat a bath with a hypoallergenic shampoo containing oatmeal or benzyl peroxide. A vinegar-water rinse can be used after the bath: add four teaspoons of white vinegar to one gallon of water. Massage this through the fur, then rinse again with plain water and dry. Cool water rinses also help calm the skin.

- Leave-on moisturizers with aloe vera and alpha keri are soothing.

- Adding 5 milligrams of zinc once daily to your cat's diet often clears up dry skin and haircoats.

- Use a humidifier or put a pan of water by your radiator to increase moisture in the air.

Dry skin is white and flaky.

COMPLEMENTARY TREATMENTS

◩ DIETARY REMEDIES
Fatty acid supplements help restore moisture to dry skin. The best sources are freshwater fish oils like salmon. Add ⅛ tsp to meals once daily.

HEARTWORM

Heartworm disease is a serious and potentially fatal condition caused by worms called *dirofilaria immitus*. These spaghetti-like worms grow up to 12 inches long, and reside in the heart. The larval form of this worm is transmitted by the bite of a mosquito. The worms generally cause severe heart and lung damage before any signs of the disease become apparent. Many cats show no signs and then suddenly die. Accurate detection and diagnosis is difficult because signs are often vague and mimic other diseases.

CAUSES

• *Dirofilaria immitus* worms living in the heart of a cat. The larval form of these worms are transmitted to cats by mosquito bites.

SYMPTOMS

• Coughing, difficulty breathing, and lethargy.

WHAT YOU AND YOUR VET CAN DO

• Outdoor cats are most susceptible, but mosquitoes can get just about anywhere, so all cats are at risk. To limit mosquito exposure, keep cats inside in the early morning and late at night when mosquitoes are most active.

• Eighty percent of infected cats have "occult" heartworm disease and display no symptoms at all. Some of these cats appear healthy and then suddenly die.

• In cats, treatment is risky, very extensive, and occasionally even fatal.

• Prevention is the key. Several new insect growth regulation products also prevent heartworm disease. For example, Selameetin, the active ingredient in a product called Revolution, is approved to prevent heartworms as well as fleas, mites, and many other parasites. It comes as a liquid, which should be applied between the shoulder blades at 30-day intervals. Cats should test negative prior to receiving preventative medication.

3

COMPLEMENTARY TREATMENTS

⊠ HERBAL REMEDIES
Alpha keri oil repels mosquitoes, smells good, and is safe. Mix 1 tsp with 1 pint water. Use as a spritz on the skin of your cat.

▢ HOMEOPATHIC REMEDIES
Sulfur 6x: 1 pellet every other day for 30 days may relieve skin irritation from mosquitoes, but it won't prevent heartworms.

HAIR LOSS

Cats can lose clumps of hair as a result of fighting or through stress. However, it is more commonly caused by itching brought about by an allergy or insect bites. Hair loss may also be an outward sign of an underlying illness, but in this case the cat will generally be quite ill by the time the coat begins to deteriorate. Cats also shed their hair seasonally, depending on the breed, but this shedding, or molting as it is known, is more irritating than dramatic.

CAUSES

• Excessive scratching (see p. 42) is the number one cause of hair loss in cats and is usually prompted by allergies. Flea bites are responsible for 90 percent of cat allergies and produce skin lesions on the head and neck of cats. Itching is also caused by inhalant allergies, and food allergies. Skin parasites, mosquitoes, and mites can also cause a cat to scratch, resulting in hair loss.

• Ringworm causes hair loss without itching.

• Hormonal imbalances like diabetes and thyroid disease can also cause hair loss. This occurs in patterns that match on each side of a cat's body.

• Psychological disorders caused by stress can result in hair loss due to overgrooming.

• Illness, fighting, and poisoning can also result in hair loss.

Some types of pedigree cat have been bred to be hairless, such as the rare Sphynx breed.

• Female cats sometimes suffer temporary loss of hair soon after giving birth.

• Seasonal thinning of the hair is quite natural, especially in the case of long-haired breeds such as the Norwegian Forest Cat. This breed loses much of its distinctive facial ruff in the spring, when the weather becomes warmer.

WHAT YOUR VET CAN DO

• Vets use the pattern of hair loss, location of lesions, the age of the cat, and the presence or absence of scratching to determine the underlying cause.

• Exact therapy will depend on the underlying problem. Relief from allergies involves removing the allergen, such as fleas, pollen, or food. Vitamin C and salmon oil relieve dry itchy skin. Allergen-free diets bring some relief from itchiness in the first 6 to 8 weeks.

• Hormone disorders are diagnosed with blood and urine tests. Levels are rebalanced accordingly. For example, insulin controls diabetes, oral medication or iodine decrease excess thyroid levels.

• Bach Flower Remedies help reduce stress as do sunshine and diet.

3

COMPLEMENTARY TREATMENTS

HERBAL REMEDIES
About 1 tsp (5ml) kelp powder sprinkled over the cat's food daily can help to boost a sluggish thyroid gland.

HOMEOPATHIC REMEDIES
2 or 3 Selenium 30c pellets crushed to powder help to promote hair growth. Give 3 doses 12 hours apart. Wait 30 days for signs of new hair growth and give no other remedies. If no response use Septin 30c at the same dosage. This treatment also helps to restore poor hair coats in cats after giving birth.

STUD TAIL

Stud tail is a greasy infection caused by the excessive secretion of oil from the sebaceous glands at the base of the tail. Normally this oil helps to repel water, making a cat's coat somewhat waterproof as well as keeping it soft. In excess, the oil causes matting of the fur and often triggers secondary infections. The condition is most common in nonneutered male cats.

SYMPTOMS

• Grease accumulates on the fur, matting it and causing it to take on a crusty appearance.
• Bacterial infections and pus may be present.

CAUSE

• Excess secretion of oil from the sebaceous glands at the base of the tail.

WHAT YOU AND YOUR VET CAN DO

• Diagnosis is based on signs. To treat stud tail remove the matted hair with clippers. Clean tail daily with benzyl peroxide or oatmeal shampoo then rinse with water. Bran removes dirt and oil from the tail and can be used to spot clean greasy areas.

• To dry out lesions, blot them with alcohol twice daily or use a solution of white vinegar with water (50/50). Antiobiotics eliminate bacterial infections.

HOW TO GIVE A BRAN BATH

Bran, which acts as a dry shampoo, can be bought from most petshops. Warm 6 oz of bran on a tray in the oven, and then tip it into a bowl. Place an old sheet or newspaper on top of a table, or where the mess you'll be making won't be a problem. Holding your cat, rub the bran into the cat's coat going against the grain of the fur. Leave the bran on for 3 minutes, then gently brush it out with a natural bristle brush. The results are excellent.

Gently rub the bran into the fur.

Brush out the bran with a soft-bristled brush.

3

FELINE ACNE

Feline acne is a skin condition caused by the excess secretion of oil, or sebum, from overactive sebacceous glands in the chin. The sebum plugs up the hair follicles in the chin, causing blackheads called comedomes to form. Secondary bacterial infections and itching can occur. Acne affects male and female cats of all ages.

CAUSES

• Excess oil from sebaceous glands on the chin blocks hair folicles, causing blackheads to form, which may become infected with bacteria.

SYMPTOMS

• Inflamed and infected skin under jaw.
• Pimples may appear.

WHAT YOU AND YOUR VET CAN DO

• Diagnosis of feline acne is usually based on signs. A warm compress held over the chin for 2 minutes twice daily helps to open pores.

• Clean the chin with benzyl peroxide, then rinse with water. Using a cotton ball soaked in a solution of white vinegar and water (50/50), or alcohol, dab the chin twice daily to help dry out the infected area.

Stroke and soothe your cat before treating the infected area.

• Do not use human acne treatments. They are toxic and cats tend to lick them off.

• Do not squeeze the pimple or lesion because this is painful and may spread the infection or prolong the time it takes for the acne to heal.

• Bacterial infections are usually treated with antibiotics by your vet.

COMPLEMENTARY TREATMENTS

⊠ HERBAL REMEDIES

Calendula tincture. speeds healing and helps clear up bacterial infections. Use six drops in 1 fl oz (30 ml) water. Dab on area twice daily with a cotton ball (discard after use).
Aloe vera gel helps soothe dry areas but should be avoided if the skin is greasy.

Aloe vera

SUNBURN

Cats naturally love to lie in the sun but excess exposure not only causes painful sunburn, it also increases the risk of skin cancer. Breeds with sparse fur like the Sphink Canadian Hairless and cats with white fur are most susceptible. A type of cancer called squamous cell carcenoma is the most prevalent type of cancer arising from sunburned skin, especially in sunworshiping white cats. The eartips are usually affected, but the nose, lip, and eyelids are also at risk.

SYMPTOMS

- Reddened areason parts of the body where the skin is directly exposed to the sun's rays, particularly the eartips, nose, lips, and eyelids.
- The skin becomes raw and irritated and may get thickened and crusty, especially on the eartips.
- The sores can open and become infected. Cats may scratch them, and resist being touched on affected areas.

CAUSE

- Overexposure to sunlight.

WHAT YOU CAN DO

- To prevent sunburn, try to keep your cat out of the sun when it is at its hottest between 10 am and 3 pm. You may also have to consider protective clothing for the cat's vunerable areas.

- If your cat becomes sunburned, it is important to provide relief without delay. The affected areas will be red and inflamed, as well as very tender, so handle the cat with particular care. The best way to cool the skin is by gently covering it with a face cloth soaked in cold or tepid water. Don't let it dry out. Repeat every 30 minutes or so for a period of between two and three hours.

- If signs of sunburn persist, ask your vet to check your cat for skin cancer.

- If squamous cell carcinoma is detected, the best therapy depends on the area involved. Most cancerous tumors occur on the eartips and surgical removal of the affected area works best to eliminate the problem. It is also a good idea to have a specialist examine the ear after surgery to help ensure that all the cancerous cells have been eliminated. Cryosurgery, which involves freezing cancerous cells, is the best way to eliminate tumors when they occur on the eyelid.

3

3

Warning

Avoid using sunscreen products made for people on your cat because many contain potentially harmful ingredients. Most cats lick off products applied to their skin and some sunscreen products contain zinc oxide, which is toxic to cats if ingested. The zinc destroys red blood cells, which can result in fatal anemia. Also toxic to cats is Benzocaine, an anesthetic available in sprays and cream, that some people use to soothe sunburned skin.

• Surgery is an effective treatment for skin cancer with most cats. However, it is worth asking your vet to give your cat a thorough examination. Diagnostics usually include blood and urine tests to determine if major organs like the liver and kidneys are still functioning normally. Chest X rays help vets determine whether or not the cancer has spread to the lungs. Diagnosis of cancer is confirmed by a biopsy. The cat is placed under anesthetic and a tiny piece of affected tissue is removed and examined under a microscope.

COMPLEMENTARY TREATMENTS

⊠ HERBAL REMEDIES

Witch hazel cools and soothes sunburned skin. Apply the lotion with a cotton ball four times daily.

Aloe Vera gel soothes and moisturizes sunburned skin. Apply to affected areas 3-4 times daly.

Witch hazel

CLAWS

Cats depend on their claws for a variety of tasks, including grooming, catching prey, defending themselves, and climbing. Cats are one of the few animals that can retract their claws, which helps to prevent unnecessary wear and tear. Their claws grow continually, and the old outer layers, called the cuticle, are shed by scratching which helps keep the tips sharp for hunting. Scratching also helps cats to spread their scent and mark their territory. Conflict arises in the home if the cat decides to use a piece of furniture for sharpening his claws, a particular problem for cats that live indoors permanently. The simplest solution is to buy a scratching post and train your cat to exercise his claws here. Issues relating to scratching are covered in Destructive Behavior (see pp. 90–91).

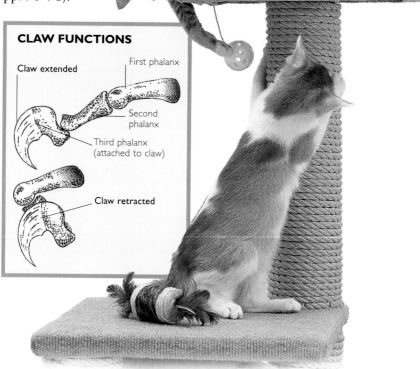

CLAW FUNCTIONS

Claw extended

First phalanx

Second phalanx

Third phalanx (attached to claw)

Claw retracted

WHAT YOU AND YOUR VET CAN DO

• Some cats are active enough to wear down their own nails but most cats need nail trims every two to four weeks to prevent overgrown nails and reduce the likelihood of damage to the home. With patience and training most cats allow nail trims. Nervous cats may need to be wrapped in a towel so that only one foot is exposed at a time. To trim your cat's nails, you can use nail trimmers made for people, but the Roscoe or "guillotine" type nail trimmer (see photograph below), available commerciallly, will make the job easier. A blood vessel runs down the center of each nail that will bleed if the nail is cut too short. This vessel is easier to see on the white nails, so start with a white nail and use it as a reference for the dark nails. Just trim the tip that curves downward so the nail remains parallel to the toe. A dew claw, located in the thumb position, is present in most cats and also needs to be trimmed. In case you trim a nail too short, have a styptic pencil (as sold for shaving cuts) or silver nitrate stick on hand to stop the bleeding. Flour, cornstarch, or baking soda, along with pressure, will also work.

• Training your cat will go a long way toward preventing destructive scratching behavior. Provide a scratching post from day one and give your cat clear messages about which objects she may or may not scratch. If verbal reprimands fail, negative reinforcement, for example a quick squirt from a water bottle or making a loud noise, may help. It is important to immediately redirect your cat's attention to an appropriate object so that she begins to differentiate and learns the rules. Until your cat has complete respect for your rules, confinement works well when supervision is not possible.

3

• If training fails, other options are available. Declawing cats is a controversial procedure that some people feel is inhumane, and some vets will not even perform it. However, there are times when this is appropriate, for example when euthenasia is the only other option. The surgery, which entails removing the nail at its base, is performed under general anesthesia and generally involves only the front feet. It can be done from 12 weeks of age. Flexor tendonectomy is another surgical procedure, which leaves the claws intact but prevents the cat from extending them. "Nail caps" are a commercially available product made of smooth plastic. They are attached to the end of the nail with a special glue and are replaced each month. This can be done by you or your vet.

If you are unsure of how to clip your cat's nails, ask your vet to show you.

ABSCESSES

Abscesses are pockets of pus under the skin. Pus is an accumulation of bacteria and white blood cells and indicates the presence of infection. Abscesses occur most frequently in unneutered tomcats that get bitten and scratched as they compete for territory. Bacteria from the rival cat's mouth enters the puncture wounds in the cat's skin. The problem is detection. Because cat fur is dense, an abscess may not be apparent until it is advanced and a large lump forms. On occasions the abscess may burst of its own accord. If the abscess is not opened and drained it makes the cat feel sick. The bacterial skin infection can spread and may become lifethreatening.

3

SYMPTOMS

- Pain, swelling, and warmth at the abscess site; occasionally the swelling is not apparent. Common sites include the face, head, and neck, the base of the tail, the back of the hind legs, and the groin.
- Draining lesions with pus surrounded by skin crusts are common in mature abscesses.
- Appetite loss, fever, and depression can occur but generally subside once the abscess ruptures and drains.

CAUSES

- Abscesses generally result from a bite by another cat. The cat's sharp, pointed canine teeth, which are located at the corners of the mouth, act like needles, injecting bacteria deep into the wound.

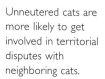

Unneutered cats are more likely to get involved in territorial disputes with neighboring cats.

WHAT YOU AND YOUR VET CAN DO

• Exact treatment depends on the size, location, and maturity of the abscess. Nondraining lesions may be allowed to mature, which can be enhanced by using warm compresses. Blood tests for feline leukemia virus (FELV) and feline immunodeficiency virus (FIV) may be necessary.

• Your vet will clip a draining lesion and flush it out with a diluted iodine-type solution. Drainage must be maintained for several days to clear the infection. Insertion of a soft rubber drainage tube may be necessary, depending on the site. The vet may prescribe antibiotics to kill the bacteria and prevent any further infection.

• Warm compresses soaked in Epsom salt applied topically for 2–3 minutes twice daily help to bring abscesses to a head.

• Neutering male cats often decreases aggressive tendencies.

3

COMPLEMENTARY TREATMENTS

If the abscess has opened and drained, you can prevent the lesion from closing prematurely by cleaning the area twice daily with hydrogen peroxide and applying propolus, a raw form of honey.

◼ HOMEOPATHIC REMEDIES

One pellet of *Silicea* 6c given on the tongue four times daily for 3–5 days may help bring an abscess to a head.

One tablet of *Hepar sulf calcareum* 30c given every four hours for three doses may provide pain relief for cats with abscesses.

◼ DIETARY REMEDIES

Sick cats need nutritional support and fluids. The following dietary supplements may provide relief for cats with abscesses suffering from fever, pain, and swelling: ¼ tsp parsley, ½ tsp raw liver, or 1 clove or capsule of garlic added to food; 250 mg vitamin C (powder) added to food twice times daily for three days.

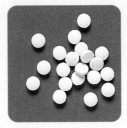

INSECT BITES AND STINGS

Summertime brings fresh air and lots of sunshine along with bees, wasps, and other flying insects. Kittens are especially vulnerable to bites and stings, being naturally curious and unaware of the hazards of snapping at flying insects and spiders. Most cats get stung on the face and the swelling can be very painful. Some cats scratch the area of a bite or sting, which can turn a swelling into a red, raw, oozing lesion. These can become infected and severe lesions can be mistaken for skin cancer.

Warning
Cats are often stung in the mouth, which is dangerous because the resulting swelling can make it difficult for them to breathe. If this happens, consult your vet immediately.

3

WHAT YOUR VET CAN DO

• Most lesions caused by bites and stings resolve within 7–10 days if cats are kept away from insects. A variety of medications are available to reduce swelling and pain. Cats lick off most products applied to the skin, so many vets use injectable medication that provides safe, effective relief. Bees leave behind the stinging apparatus and this can be carefully removed with tweezers.

COMPLEMENTARY TREATMENTS

HERBAL REMEDIES

To soothe minor stings and bites, apply a *calendula officinalis* (marigold) compress to the affected area. Add six drops of tincture to 2 tbsp (30 ml) of water and soak a gauze pad in the mixture. Then tape the gauze carefully in place over the wound.

To give instant relief for bee stings, break open the stem of a dandelion and rub the milk onto the sting. A paste of baking soda and water also works.

SYSTEMIC ILLNESSES

Systemic illness is defined as a disease of any major organ system or any condition that ultimately affects the whole body. The signs will vary depending on which organ system is involved, for instance the heart, liver, or kidneys. The keys to making sure your cat has the greatest possible quality and length of life are early recognition and reduction of any predisposing health risk factors, as well as accurate diagnosis and prompt correction. The more observant you are as an owner, the easier it will be for you to work with your vet to ensure your cat's optimal health.

4

AGING

Aging begins when the body's systems start to slow down—when cells deteriorate faster than the body can repair them. We think of it as a progressive decline in mental and physical functioning and appearance, which is accompanied by an increase in susceptibility to chronic diseases. This is caused primarily by several factors including oxidative stress and malnutrition. The aging process generally begins at maturity, somewhere between eight and ten months old in cats. In human terms, cats age 15–20 years in their first year and four years for each year thereafter. So a 10-year-old cat is the equivalent age of a person of about 50 years. However, as with humans, age related changes vary with each individual, and are determined as much by how a cat eats, moves, and feels as by his or her chronological age.

CAUSES

• The natural metabolic processes of the body as well as toxins in the environment subject animals to the damaging effects of harmful compounds called free radicals, which increase as a cat ages. These highly toxic molecules damage your cat's DNA (genetic material) and proteins and make them more susceptible to cancer, corrode their arteries, and increase their risk of heart disease. This process, known as oxidative stress, causes your cat's body to deteriorate in much the same way as oxygen causes iron to rust.

• Malnutrition jeopardizes the health, longevity, and performance of cats. Malnutrition is defined as any nutritional disorder in which nutrients are unbalanced or inadequate.

WHAT YOU AND YOUR VET CAN DO

• The longer and more consistently you provide an optimally balanced diet, the greater your cat's chances of living a long healthy life. Dietary hints are given on page 26.

With a little extra care, cats can lead healthy lives well into their mid-twenties.

4

Taking senior cats for a checkup with a vet at least twice a year is the best way of ensuring any disorder benefits from early detection and treatment.

• Antioxidants are the body's natural defense against free radicals. In addition to fending off free radicals, they also help protect cell membranes and DNA. Antioxidants, include Vitamins A, C, and E; minerals like selenium; and other agents such as coenzyme Q10. They decrease the level of oxidative stress and can be prescribed in specific formulas for pets as needed.

• Essential fatty acids including omega 3, omega 6, and gamma linoleic acid help cats maintain a proper fatty balance as the body's fatty acid synthesis naturally decreases with age. These compounds found in freshwater fish and fish oils promote a healthy skin and haircoat and add a great shine. They also help to prepare some cats to better tolerate skin sensitivities.

4

• Try to make sure that your cat gets 10 minutes' exercise twice a day. This is important for weight control and overall health, especially for the heart and lungs. Regular exercise also increases muscle tone, enhances agility, and improves blood circulation.

• Sick, arthritic, or obese cats can't groom themselves properly, so take a little extra time combing and brushing your cat. Trim your cat's nails every two weeks because many older cats do not use scratching posts regularly.

COMPLEMENTARY TREATMENTS

▢ HOMEOPATHIC REMEDIES
Rhus tox 6x helps to relieve arthritis when a cat is stiff in the morning, but loosens up during the day. Use 1 pellet each day for 30 days.

▰ DIETARY REMEDIES
Glucosamine sulfate is a nutritional supplement that helps to relive pain in the joints. Give 20 mg twice a day. Often given with 25 mg of MSM.

HORMONAL DISORDERS

The hormonal or endocrine system is made up of seven glands that produce substances called hormones, which travel to different parts of the body and stimulate a response. Disorders occur when the glands produce either too much or too little of a particular hormone. The most common hormonal disorders in cats are diabetes mellitus, where an inadequate response to the hormone insulin causes cats to develop high blood sugar levels, and hyperthyroidism, which results from an excess of thyroid hormone levels in older cats and affects their metabolism.

SYMPTOMS

Diabetes mellitus:
• Excessive urination.
• Excessive drinking.
• Increased appetite.
• Weight loss.
• Initially cats remain active and alert, but they may later develop recurring infections, often of the urinary tract and/or skin.
• Nerve damage can occur causing diabetic neuropathy.

Hyperthyroidism:
• Increased appetite.
• Matted and scruffy coat.
• Thyroid glands increase in size.
• Increased thirst, often linked with diarrhea and vomiting.
• Unexplained weight loss.

Hypothyroidism:
(A rare condition caused by a thyroid deficiency)
• Weight gain.
• Sensitivity to cold.
• Lethargy.
• Thinning coat and scaly skin.

CAUSES

• Diabetes mellitus is defined as a "dysfunction" in the amount, availability, and/or biological activity of insulin, which is secreted by the pancreas. This results in excess blood sugar levels and many other disorders. The exact cause is not known but obesity, genetics and pancreatic disease may be predisposing factors.

• The underlying cause of many thyroid disorders is unknown. In some cats, cancer is responsible. Secondary heart and kidney disease often occur as a result of thyroid problems.

4

WHAT YOU AND YOUR VET CAN DO

• Diagnosis of diabetes is based on signs, as well as blood and urine tests that show elevated blood sugar levels. There is no cure, but insulin replacement is an effective control. Insulin requirements can change and must be monitored daily for life. Too much or too little insulin can cause life-threatening seizures. A small percentage of cats revert back to a normal non-diabetic state with weight reduction and need no further therapy or insulin.

• The majority of diabetic cats are treated with daily insulin injections given under the skin. Controlling diet and exercise along with neutering helps to keep insulin needs consistent. Obese cats must loose weight gradually. High-fiber (10–15 percent) low-fat diets work well. Omega 3 fatty acids should not be added to the diets of diabetic cats as they can increase blood sugar levels.

• A variety of oral medications that decrease blood sugar are available. Most are relatively safe and effective for diabetic cats that are relatively healthy.

• Hyperthyroidism is diagnosed with a blood test that detects increased levels of thyroid hormone. Most cases are not curable but can be controlled.

• Therapy for hyperthyroidism varies with the underlying cause of the thyroid disorder, the cat's age, and whether other problems like heart or kidney disease exist. Oral Tapazole tablets given daily are the most effective and inexpensive solution for some cats. Radiotherapy using radioactive iodine injections to destroy abnormal thyroid tissue is considered by many people to be the best treatment available, but it is very expensive. Surgical removal of the diseased thyroid may be necessary if cancer is the underlying cause, but the procedure is difficult and dangerous in old cats, and not necessarily effective.

COMPLEMENTARY TREATMENTS

4

☑ DIETARY REMEDIES

Food and supplements geared to stabilizing blood sugar and increasing the body's sensitivity to insulin include: broccoli and tomatoes, a source of a mineral called vanadium, which helps stabilize blood sugar.

Coenzyme Q10: give a 10 mg dose three times daily.
Vitamin C powder: 250 mg given three times daily. Vitamin E 400 IU capsule: once a week mix contents of capsule with meal. Pancreatic glandulars are pancreatic cells sold at grocery stores and are a potential source of insulin. Increase dietry fiber by adding one tsp chopped alfalfa sprouts, or half tsp of oat bran, or one tsp of grated raw zucchini or carrots, or one tsp cooked green beans or squash. Sprinkle cool dill or parsley tea over the cat's food. Many commercial foods are specifically formulated for diabetic cats.

Parsley tea

LIVER PROBLEMS

The liver is one of the most important organs. It detoxifies or removes harmful substances from the foods we eat and eliminates them in a substance called bile. A cat's liver is unable to detoxify some products, such as aspirin, which are harmless to humans. If a cat eats these products, they can be fatal. There are also three common liver diseases that affect cats. Fatty liver disease, is a condition in which excess fat accumulates in the liver. This can result in liver failure and the condition is fatal without prompt treatment. Cholangitis is a chronic inflammation of the bile ducts, which may progress to cholangiohepatitis, a chronic inflammation of the bile ducts and the liver.

SYMPTOMS

Fatty liver disease
- Sustained appetite loss.
- Weight loss.
- Depression.
- Jaundice—a yellowish discoloration of the whites of the eyes and skin.
- Toxic levels of ammonia can accumulate in the the brain due to liver failure, which can result in siezures and comas.

Cholangiohepatitis
- Lack of appetite.
- Weight loss.
- Occasional fevers.
- Vomiting
- Anemia

CAUSES

- Fatty liver disease occurs because of anything causing a cat to stop eating such as dental and kidney problems, diabetes, cat flu, anxiety etc.

- Cholangitis and/or cholangiohepatitis are usually caused by unknown factors. Immune system disorders, bacterial infections and, rarely, pancreatic upsets can be responsible.

WHAT YOU AND YOUR VET CAN DO

- Your vet may have to perform a tissue biopsy of the liver to determine the type of liver disease.

- Aggressive forcefeeding through a surgically placed stomach tube is the simplest, most effective treatment for cats suffering from fatty liver disease. Owners can easily feed high-protein, kitten-type diets through the tube at home.

- Cholangiohepatitis is often treated with the drug Astigal to block the inflamatory reaction and antibiotics to eliminate bacterial causes.

YOUR CAT'S DIGESTIVE ORGANS

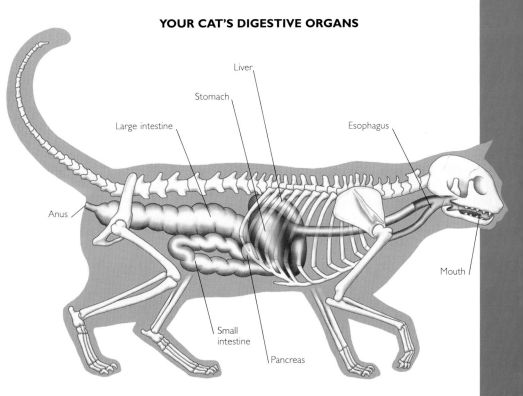

Liver

Stomach

Large intestine

Esophagus

Anus

Mouth

Small intestine

Pancreas

COMPLEMENTARY TREATMENTS

4

◪ DIETARY REMEDIES
Vitamin supplements are beneficial for cats with both hepatitis and fatty liver disease. Vitamins A, C, and E are antioxidants that can be mixed with meals. Argine stimulates natural immunity. Carnite increases energy and vitamin C production.

Vitamin C is a good antioxidant

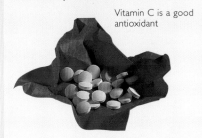

▦ HOMEOPATHIC REMEDIES
Belladonna 6x (deadly nightshade), is recommended when your cat has a fever and is agitated. One pellet every 4 hours on the tongue for up to five days or until signs are gone. Allow no food 10 minutes before or after. Stop the treatment if the cat is no better after first 24 hours.

▦ BACH FLOWER REMEDIES
Use crabapple to cleanse the body, impatiens if the cat seems angry, aspen if the cat is fearful. Squeeze three drops into the cat's mouth three times daily, or mix with its water or a meal.

KIDNEY PROBLEMS

The kidneys filter and remove toxic waste products from the cat's blood via the urine. They also regulate calcium and vitamin D levels, maintain the cat's level of hydration, and secrete the hormone responsible for red blood cell production. Acute kidney disease occurs suddenly but, with prompt recognition and treatment, it is generally reversible. This disease is rare in cats, unlike chronic kidney disease, which occurs as the kidneys deteriorate slowly over a cat's lifetime. This is a most common situation and is called chronic renal disease (CRD). CRD is not reversible and the signs generally don't occur until 80 percent of the cat's kidney function is lost.

CAUSES

• Most usual cause of CRD is age-related deterioration of the kidneys.

• Diabetes and thyroid disease.

• Nutritional inbalances

• Immune system defects such as leukemia, feline immunodeficiency virus, or cancer.

• Toxins such as antifreeze.

• Inherited defect in some breeds, for example, the Abyssinian.

4

Long-term excessive urination and excessive drinking are the most common initial signs of chronic kidney failure.

WHAT YOU AND YOUR VET CAN DO

• Routine lab tests of blood and urine do not reveal CRD until 75 to 80 percent of kidney function is lost. However, X ray, ultrasound scans can be used to aid diagnosis.

• A biopsy confirms the exact diagnosis. A tiny piece of liver tissue and/or cells is removed and examined under the microscope.

• Fluid therapy to correct dehydration is the single most important factor in treatment. Without normal kidney function toxins like ammonia, which are normally eliminated in the urine build up in the blood and cause serious damage like vomiting, diarrhea, appetite loss, anemia, heart problems, and dementia. Fluids are given under the skin or through a catheter (tube) inserted into a vein. Some owners learn to give fluids at home. Dialysis machines that filter toxins from the blood and kidney transplants are available in extreme cases.

• Special diets with restricted levels of protein and phosphorus reduce the toxic waste load on the kidneys.

• Calcitrol is a form of activated Vitamin D, (a hormone) that helps prevent progression of kidney disease. It is given by mouth daily and is excellent. Ambodipine (Norvasc R) safely reduces blood pressure when necessary to prevent hypertension. Tumil-K is a potassium source that is often low in these cats due to lack of appetite. Appetite stimulants may also be needed.

SYMPTOMS

Early signs include
• Excessive urination and drinking.
• Dehydration
• Later, weight loss, vomiting, depression and appetite loss occur.

4

COMPLEMENTARY TREATMENTS

◪ DIETARY REMEDIES
B vitamins and iron help combat anemia, which is often present with CRD because it is the kidneys that normally make the hormones that stimulate red blood cell production.

◪ HERBAL REMEDIES
Kombu broth is made of a seaweed rich in minerals and low in sodium. Parsley tea is high in minerals, vitamins A,B, C, and potassium. Horsetail grass infusion is also beneficial.

◪ HOMEOPATHIC REMEDIES
Relief can be provided by apis mellifica 10m. Four doses administered at hourly intervals are normally recommended. Apis mellifica should be avoided if your cat is pregnant.

Apis mellifica is made from the honey bee.

URINARY TRACT PROBLEMS

Urine forms in the kidneys, is stored in the urinary bladder, then passes through a narrow tube called the urethra, and is eliminated. Feline Lower Urinary Tract Disease (FLUTD) is a common group of conditions affecting the urinary bladder and/or urethra in neutered cats. FLUTD is common in cats that are around four years old, but it can also affect cats that are over ten years old.

An electron micrograph of a bladder stone.

CAUSES

• Bacterial or viral infection.

• Dehydration.

• Stress.

• Plugs of sandy material in the urethra.

• The cause of FLUTD in a young cat is unkown in over half the cases.

• The majority of older cats with this disorder also suffer from chronic kidney failure. Many have urine infections and/or bladder stones. A few have a blocked urethra.

WHAT YOU AND YOUR VET CAN DO

• The vet will diagnose the problem, based on the history, signs, along with blood and urine tests, and X rays in older cats.

• It is vital that your cat should have constant access to clean, fresh water.

• Treatment is focused on managing the diet to help minimize recurrent urinary problems. Canned diets are moister than dry diets, and can be better.

• Many prescription diets formulated for FLUTD are available. Analysis of urine is important, especially if crystals are present, because many of these prescription diets are geared to acidify PH of urine, which can make the problem worse.

• Many cats with unknown cause of FLUTD respond to the antidepressant Elavil. It relieves bladder inflammation and pain and decreases anxiety.

• Antibiotics eliminate bacterial urinary infections if present.

> ### Warning
>
> Cats unable to urinate for 24 to 48 hours because of a urethral blockage risk death. Cats with FLUTD show similar signs despite a wide variety of potential causes. Female spayed cats often urinate outside the litter box and occassionally there is blood in the urine. Neutered male cats make several unsuccessful trips to the litter box, strain to urinate, and may cry out in pain. Many of them also lick their genital area excessively.

4

THE URINARY SYSTEM

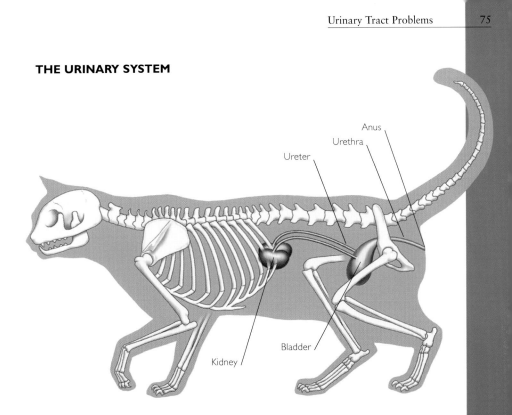

Anus

Urethra

Ureter

Kidney

Bladder

COMPLEMENTARY TREATMENTS

☒ HERBAL REMEDIES

Diuretic herbs such as parsley, corn silk and dandelion promote urination. Flushing the urinary tract can help to eliminate small bladder stones,

toxins and bacteria. Mix 1 tsp in meals twice daily.

▨ DIETARY REMEDIES

To help acidify your cat's urine, give 1 tsp of concentrated cranberry juice twice a day. Cranberry is bacteriostatic and can help to prevent recurrent urinary infections. Nutrients containing glycosaminoglycans or "gags" line the bladder and promote healing.

▣ HOMEOPATHIC REMEDIES

Canthans 30c is beneficial for male cats making constant attempts to urinate, licking penis and vocalizing pain. Give 1 pellet at 15 minute intervals for three treatments.

4

VIRAL DISEASES

Viruses often cause severe long-term illness because they interfere with a cat's natural ability to ward off infection. The leading viral killer of cats today is feline leukemia (FELV). The virus, which is spread by prolonged cat-to-cat contact and through bite wounds, is shed in saliva, tears, urine, and feces. Fifty percent of cats infected with FELV die of secondary infections and many develop a cancer of the tissue known as lymphosarcoma. Feline immunodeficiency virus (FIV), also known as feline AIDS, is another lethal viral disease. It is usually spread through bite wounds, so aggressive cats are most at risk. Like feline lukemia, FIV impairs the immune system, leaving infected cats prone to secondary infections, which are the major cause of death.

WHAT YOU AND YOUR VET CAN DO

• Blood tests accurately detect FELV and FIV.

• There is no cure for either of these diseases. All cases are ultimately fatal. A cat infected with FELV can live for months to years. Cats with FIV rarely survive more than two years. Some anticancer medications produce temporary remission.

• Several experimental antiviral products have been developed that extend and improve the lives of infected cats. These are safer than anticancer therapies. The most successful of these new therapies is an oral solution called human alpha interferon, which must be prescribed by your vet. Although this is not yet approved, it has been shown to stimulate the immune system and slow viral replication. Squirt 30 units per day in mouth for seven days on, seven days off. Interferon should be used along with L-Lysine tablets, available at health food stores. Crush 250 mg to powder and mix into the cat's meal twice daily.

• Epogen hormone can be injected to boost red blood cell production in order to combat severe anemia. (A vet must prescribe this.)

• Vaccination helps to prevent leukemia.

• Neutering helps decrease aggressive tendencies, and reduces the risk of the viruses being spread.

4

SYMPTOMS

FELV
• Pale gum color instead of normal bright pink.
• Anemia.
• Depression.
• Appetite loss.
• Weight loss.

FIV
• Severe chronic gum disease (gingivitis) and recurrent mouth infections.
• Appetite loss, poor haircoat, and fever.
• Late in disease, weight loss and severe wasting occur.

Warning

Cats apparently recovered from FELV and FIP can act as carriers and spread the disease. Diseases that suppress the immune system can also reactivate. To lower risk of infection disinfect house with bleach, which kills the viruses.

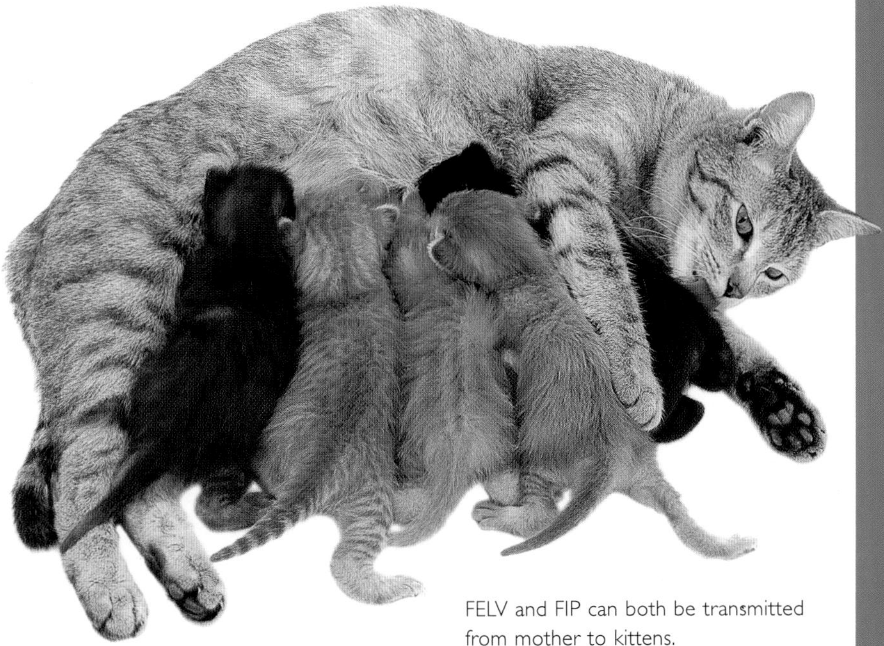

FELV and FIP can both be transmitted from mother to kittens.

Complementary treatments

Herbal remedies

Herbs that stimulate immunity include astralagus, echinacea, and reishi—a mushroom that strengthens the body.

Dietary remedies

A balanced diet supplemented with B vitamins and iron can help to prevent anemia. Nutritional yeast is a good source of B vitamins—add ⅛ teaspoon per meal. Raw liver is a source of both iron and B vitamins. Add one minced teaspoon to meals three times weekly. Vitamins A, C, and E added to meals help to stimulate immunity. Dosage: vitamin A, 10,000 IU weekly; vitamin C, 250 millgrams three times daily; vitamin E, 400 IU weekly.

Fish oil or other omega 3 fatty acid sources appear to reduce cancer spread, and enhance natural defenses. To combat cancer feed your cat a diet with increased levels of fats and high quality proteins (beef and chicken) which is low in carbohydrates (grains and rice).

Homeopathic remedies

Natrum mariaticum 6x is a salt that helps mouth ulcers to heal. Mix ¼ teaspoon of the salt into ½ cup of water and flush out the cat's mouth. The cat's head should be kept down to prevent the cat from swallowing the solution.

HEART PROBLEMS

The heart is the most important organ in the body. Its function is to collect oxygen-poor blood from the body and pump it into the lungs, where it picks up oxygen. The heart then pumps the oxygen-rich blood back out into the body. Hypertrophic cardiomyopathy (HCM) is the most common heart disease in cats. HCM affects heart muscle function, damaging the heart's ability to pump blood effectively. Blood circulation is impaired and the body is deprived of oxygen and vital nutrients. A growing number of heart failures in cats are caused by heartworm disease (see p.53), which has been reported in all 50 states and is also a problem in many other countries where mosquitoes exist.

SYMPTOMS

- Signs of HCM vary, and in many cases there are no signs at all prior to a sudden death.
- Some cats may become shy and hide a lot.
- Increasing breathing difficulty related to the severity of the heart failure.
- Lethargy, appetite loss, and fainting may occur.
- Paralysis of hind legs occurs when blood clots form.

4

CAUSES

• Primary HCM is caused by a genetic mutation in the heart muscle cells of certain breeds, including the Main Coon and the American Short Hair, and usually affects cats from two to five years old.

• Secondary HCM can result from hypertension, hyperthyroidism, and chronic kidney disease. In these cases, when the primary problem is treated, the HCM usually resolves.

• Another, now rare, form of cardiomyopathy can be caused by taurine deficient diets, historically caused by cats being fed dog food.

• Heartworm disease.

• Bacteria from gum disease.

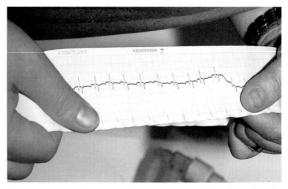

Electrocardiographs record the electrical activity of the heart.

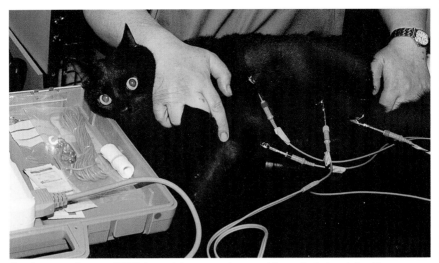

An electrocardiogram (EGG) is a painless procedure used to evaluate heart function.

WHAT YOU AND YOUR VET CAN DO

• An echocardiogram (EGG) is the single best way to determine heart function and diagnose the cause of a heart problem.

• Therapy is geared to help the heart function more efficiently, prevent further heart muscle damage, and decrease the risk of blood clot formation.

• Medication used includes Digitalis, which improves heart muscle function.

• A diet that is low in sodium and diuretics like lasix help to prevent excess fluid accumulating in the lungs. This can occur as a result of heart disease and makes breathing difficult.

• Blood clots are a sign of severe heat failure and are a true life and death emergency. Dilators help to enlarge the veins, allowing the blood to flow more easily, but clots tend to recur and often cause death within a few months.

• A 10 milligram dose of coenzyme Q10 added to meals once daily helps to support heart function.

4

COMPLEMENTARY TREATMENTS

⊠ HERBAL REMEDIES

Parsley tea can be given in conjunction with a diuretic to increase fluid loss from the body. Add a few sprigs of parsley to boiling water. Allow to stand for 10 minutes. Strain and allow to cool. Pour 1 tbsp (15 ml) of the tea over the cat's food.

⊿ DIETARY REMEDIES

Diets geared to support heart muscle function are helpful in cats with heart problems. Omega 3 fatty acids, found in fish oil and flaxseed oil, are a useful addition to a low-sodium diet. Add ⅛ teaspoon to meals.

ANEMIA

Anemia results from a low number of red blood cells in the circulation. Red blood cells normally carry oxygen and vital nutrients to all tissues of the body. Anemia can occur because not enough red blood cells are produced, or because excess numbers are lost through infestation by bloodsucking parasites or hemorrhaging, or are destroyed because of a disease.

SYMPTOMS

- Lack of energy.
- Pale gums and eye membranes.

CAUSES

- Infestations of bloodsucking parasites, such as fleas, lice, or mites. It is important to detect this early in kittens since the blood loss can be fatal.

- Viruses such as feline leukemia virus or FIV (see p. 76).

- Kidney disease (see p. 72).

- Hemorrhage or trauma causing blood loss.

- Eating onions, toxins, zinc, and copper causes loss of red blood cells and can result in anemia.

WHAT YOU AND YOUR VET CAN DO

- The vet will take a blood or urine sample to determine the severity of the problem, and give an appropriate treatment. X rays can also help diagnosis.

- For parasite infestion, treatment involves eliminating the underlying cause.

- Epogen, an injectable form of the hormone erythropoletin, made by the kidneys, allieviates kidney disorders by stimulating red blood cell production.

Vaccination (see p. 11) will afford some protection against leukemia, which is potentially fatal.

- If the anemia is severe, then a blood transfusion may be necessary.

COMPLEMENTARY TREATMENTS

✔ HOMEOPATHIC REMEDIES
Chena officinalis 6c, one pellet daily for 30 days, helps to restore strength after blood loss.

✔ DIETARY REMEDIES
A good diet providing B vitamins and iron can help to prevent anemia. Give 1 tsp of chopped raw liver once a week.

4

BEHAVIORAL PROBLEMS

As with most animals, the character of cats varies, both between individuals and between different breeds. You should take this into consideration when choosing a pet. Generally, cats are self-sufficient, clean, and quiet, but behavioral problems can arise. This is less likely if you choose a kitten; she can be encouraged from the start to behave properly in the home and toward other pets. If your cat is older, there are ways of dealing with behavioral problems, especially if you can find out the underlying cause. For example, if she was mistreated in the past she may have developed a fear of people. If you are taking a cat from a rescue group, get as much of its history as possible.

5

SOCIALIZATION

Socialization is learning to become adjusted or adapted to the world you live in. In the case of a cat the key is helping her to become familiar with people, other animals, and things in her surroundings. Properly socialized kittens usually grow up to be well-adjusted cats.

WHAT YOU CAN DO

• It is important to realize that the primary socialization period, that is, the time when kittens are most receptive to learning begins at two weeks of age, peaks at four to five weeks, and ends when the kittens are just seven weeks old. Kittens need to be with their mother until they are eight weeks old. After that, the way kittens react to their new environment depends a lot on the environment you provide and varies with their individual personality.

• When you are choosing a kitten, do not pick the boldest, most aggressive kitten in the litter, and avoid the timid ones that hide and crouch in the corner. Choose an average kitten that seems to be friendly, walks up to you, wants to be picked up, and seems to enjoy being handled. This type of kitten usually makes the best kind of pet when it grows up.

• Before you bring home a new kitten, you will need to kitty proof your home, making your home and yard as safe as possible. Kittens can get into anything and can make a toy out of almost anything. A lot of what they see goes into their mouth, especially while new teeth are developing. Look at your home from a kitten's perspective to locate potentially dangerous temptations such as electric cords, dangling wires, rubber bands, anything shiny like tinsel, and plants that may be toxic. Remove them, placing them out of reach of your kitten.

• Kittens are like children; if you leave them in a room alone, they will probably grow up to be shy and timid. Similarly, if you overprotect and deny them exposure to the outside world, they will grow up to be fearful, antisocial, and problematic. If you

African wild cats are the ancestors of today's house cats.

5

Many cats enjoy going for walks. A harness and leash, rather than a collar, usually work best.

socialize your kitten from day one, she will be more likely to grow up to be a happy, well-adjusted adult cat.

• To socialize your kitten, take her everywhere you go, introducing her to as many new people, places, sights, sounds, and smells as you can.

• Play plenty of games with your kitten. Some experts recommend scheduling play periods. Keep playtimes brief and avoid rough games because overstimulating very young kittens can promote aggressive tendencies.

• Toys provide a positive outlet for energetic, curious kittens. Many toys are educational and stimulate kittens mentally. Toys also help prevent boredom, destruction, and anxiety. Most cats like toys that stimulate their natural instincts. Chasing toy birds, mice, and fish that dangle, dart, and swing are favorites. To provide your kitten with variety and fresh challenges, get at least 12 toys and rotate them every few days.

COMPLEMENTARY TREATMENTS

5

🔲 HOMEOPATHIC REMEDIES
Bach Flower Remedies can help to alleviate stress. Two drops directly into the mouth is usual, up to 3 times a day. Antianxiety medications can also be given, but first talk to your vet or behaviorist.

TRAINING

Making sure that your kitten starts out in life the right way from day one will help to prevent many behavioral problems from developing at a later stage. Despite our best efforts, however, certain problems that require treatment may develop. Behavioral modification methods vary according to the specific case.

WHAT YOU AND YOUR VET CAN DO

• If you are lucky enough to start out with a kitten, teaching her good habits from the minute she walks through the door on day one is your best bet. By giving her a toy to play with, a post to scratch, and a litter box to use, you are teaching her what is appropriate to play with, and where it is acceptable for her to scratch and do her business.

• Using positive reinforcement helps achieve the best results. Observe your cat's natural behavior and figure out what she likes the best—a toy, a treat, or affection—and use that to reward correct behavior.

• If you see your kitten doing something wrong, use negative reinforcement to stop her right away. Some cats respond best to a squirt of water, others to a loud noise. Do not look at your kitten while you perform this action so that she links the unpleasant sensation with her action and not with you. Then direct your kitten's attention to an appropriate toy or activity.

• Cats do not respond well to physical punishment.

5

This posture, with ears flattened to the head, is typical of a frightened or stressed cat.

• To dissuade your kitten from scratching furniture and chewing electrical wiring or houseplants, you can dab these items with perfume. Cats dislike strong smelling scents, and this "obnoxious stimuli" will encourage your kitten to avoid these objects.

• If you do encounter a persistent behavioral problem with a kitten or cat of any age, it is important to get help. Talk to your vet, who can check for any underlying medical conditions that may be the cause. Generally a thorough medical examination is required.

• If no medical problems are responsible for the behavioral problems, referral to a behavioral specialist is the next step. Behavioralists try to pinpoint the exact problem and the stimulus (the trigger of the bad behavior), and then recommend a strategy for behavioral modification according to the specific nature of the problem. They will need a detailed written history and a home visit is recommended, although telephone consultations are available.

COMPLEMENTARY TREATMENTS

🖾 HOMEOPATHIC REMEDIES

It is important to try to prevent the causes of stress as much as possible, but you may not always be able to do so. If your cat is injured in a fight, then *Arnica montana* 6c (leopard's bane) can bring relief.

🌺 BACH FLOWER REMEDIES

Use the Bach Rescue Remedy, made of cherry plum, clematis, impatiens, rock rose, and star of Bethlehem to help calm down a stressed cat.

5

LITTER BOX PROBLEMS

Failing to use the litter box is the behavioral problem in cats that pet owners find most upsetting and is the leading reason why cat owners have their cat put down. Before a psychological cause can be diagnosed, all potential medical problems must be ruled out by your vet. Feline lower urinary tract disorder (FLUTD) is the leading medical cause. Inappropriate eliminiation is the term used when behavioral problems cause cats not to use their litter box. These are frequently linked to either urine spraying behavior (see p. 88), or litter aversion.

CAUSES

• Feline lower urinary tract disease (FLUTD; see p. 74).

• Urine spraying, may begin when kittens become sexually mature (at five to six months). This is natural behavior with a hormonal influence that is usually solved by neutering.

• The introduction of another pet to the household can result in urine spraying. This territorial marking activity occurs when a cat feels threatened.

• Litter aversion is a problem in which the cat does not use the litter box but defecates and/or urinates on other surfaces, for example beds, bathtubs, or rugs. If your cat eliminates just outside the box, then she probably dislikes either the

Nervous cats in particular are likely to be dissuaded by a lack of privacy, so a hooded litter tray is recommended.

litter box, or the litter inside it. If she eliminates somewhere else, it may be because she would prefer to have the litter box in a different place. Shy cats prefer privacy, but at the same time do not like to feel trapped.

• Some older cats, especially those suffering from arthritis, which makes movement painful, may find it difficult and uncomfortable to step over the sides of the litter box, so they soil the area nearby instead.

5

WHAT YOU CAN DO

• Take your cat to the vet to rule out feline lower urinary tract disease. Treatment is necessary and it can be life-threatening in neutered males.

• For cats that regularly eliminate in a wrong place outside the litter box, spraying this place with an "obnoxious stimuli" makes this area less appealing and may prompt your cat to use the litter box. "Obnoxious stimuli" are strong odors such as oil of wintergreen or menthol.

• If your cat eliminates just ouside the litter box, try changing the type of litter. Most cats like the fine silaceous clumping litter. A depth of ½ to ¾ of an inch of soft, granular, unscented litter works best. If your cat is an outdoor cat coming to live inside, try filling the tray with potting soil.

• Litterboxes should fit your cat's size. Avoid putting the box where your cat eats or sleeps; in cold, dark basements; or in busy, noisy areas. Some cats feel more secure in an open litter box accessible from three sides, while others like litter boxes with covers.

• It is essential to keep the litter box clean. Scoop out the box daily, especially after the cat has used it. Replace all the litter every 3–5 days.

• Even in a multi-cat household, it is best to provide one box per cat.

Warning

Don't use ammonia-based products to clean up your cat's urine mistakes. Urine contains ammonia, so these generally make the problem worse, because the cat may become even more attracted to the spot.

Cats are sensitive animals, and they need to feel safe and secure while they relieve themselves. Make sure their litter box is in a relatively quiet spot.

5

URINE SPRAYING

Urine spraying occurs with sexual maturity, at about six months of age, primarily in nonneutered male cats. Normally, cats urinate squatting but spraying is done on vertical surfaces while standing. Outdoors, male cats spray on prominent landmarks such as fence posts, to mark their territory and make their presence known. Female cats may also spray when they are ready to breed. Their urine contains chemicals called pheromones, which attract males in the neighborhood. Indoors, cats generally do not spray if they have been neutered unless they become stressed. Major sources of stress include overcrowding and territorial disputes.

CAUSES

• A cat's instinctive need to mark its territory.

• Spraying can also be due to stress or anxiety.

WHAT YOU AND YOUR VET CAN DO

• Neutering cats at five to six months of age prevents most spraying problems.

• For female cats, spaying generally resolves the problem, as well as preventing unwanted kittens from being born.

• You should realize that surgery may not immediately overcome the problem of spraying. In older cats, it takes six weeks for hormone levels to decrease and time is needed for the learned behavior pattern to be forgotten.

• Avoid stress in your home to help prevent urine spraying from becoming a problem. Do not overcrowd indoor cats. Give each cat his

5

Warning

Urine spray has an unpleasant odor that can be difficult to get rid of. Rubbing a soft cloth on a cat's cheek collects odor from his scent glands. Dabbing this cloth on new items of furniture may help to prevent spraying and help the cat feel more secure.

own personal space in which he can curl up. Also provide each cat with his own litter box, food bowl, and water bowl. Avoid abrupt changes in your home. Try to stick to a routine and do not rush introductions between new cats or between a cat and a new dog.

• Responsibility for triggering spraying may lie with you if you have previously come in contact with another cat that has twined itself around your legs and left a scent that is discernible to your pet. Its territorial instinct will take over and he may spray a chair leg, for example, in your vicinity.

• When you move house, check whether the previous occupants owned a cat, because this can cause repeated spraying as your cat tries to mask the scent left by its predecessor. Prevention is the simplest answer in this case. You should throw out small rugs and have all other carpeting or flooring cleaned thoroughly using products that get rid of the smell of urine such as Elim Odor, and K.O.E.

Neutering cats at a young age prevents most urine spraying.

• Feliway™ is an artificial pheromone spray from France approved for reducing urine spraying.

• Bach Flower Remedies are helpful in treating behavioral disorders in cats. Use minulus on a cat who is afraid of losing home or possessions, and holly on a jealous or suspicious cat. If you have a cat who appears terrified of his surroundings, use rock rose to overcome the fear.

5

DESTRUCTIVE BEHAVIOR

Scratching is a natural grooming behavior that keeps your cat's claws in good shape and is another way in which cats mark their territory. Unfortunately, it can also ruin your furniture and destroy your home. Cats, and especially kittens, might also chew on houseplants. This is both destructive and potentially dangerous to your pet.

WHAT YOU CAN DO

• To prevent the development of bad scratching habits, get a new scratching post when you get a kitten. Loosely woven fabrics like hemp and sisal rope are best for cats to rake their claws on. Barewood and cardboard are best for cats to pick their claws on. Do not cover the post in carpet, because your kitten will not recognize the difference between that carpet and the one in the living room. Posts can either be vertical or horizontal, but must be sturdy so that your kitten feels secure when using it.

• Teach your kitten to use her scratching post. Sit with her when she sniffs it, place her paws on it, and praise her when she uses it.

Your kitten's mother is her best teacher, so before buying a kitten ask the owner if his mother uses a scratching post regularly.

5

• Placing toys near the scratching post and rubbing it with catnip encourages your kitten to use the post.

• If your cat does not use her scratching post, figure out when she scratches the most. It may be when she wakes up or when you, her owner, come home. If you put the scratching post near the cat's sleeping area or at the front door she may be more inclined to use it.

• Insecurity may cause your cat to scratch. Rub your cat's cheek with a soft cloth, then dab the cloth on areas that she scratches. When your cat smells her own scent, she feels more secure and may stop scratching.

• Use booby traps such as balloons on areas your cat is scratching so she startles herself. Squirt water or make a sudden loud noise to stop your cat scratching if you catch her in the act.

TRIMMING OPTIONS

• Weekly trims make nails too dull to do damage (see p. 61).

• Apply plastic nail caps every six to eight weeks.

• Surgical options to discuss with your vet include a tendonectomy or declawing (see p. 61), which will eliminate the scratching problem. Both procedures are controversial but are better than keeping your cat outside or taking her to an animal shelter.

CONTROLLING PLANT EATING

• Toxic plants (see p. 100) should be removed from the environment wherever possible or placed in areas to which your cat does not have access.

• Dabbing the leaves of nontoxic plants with hot pepper sauce and spraying strong odors like cologne, menthol, or oil of wintergreen around them provide obnoxious stimuli that cats detest. They associate the bad smell with the nasty taste of the pepper and avoid items with that scent in future.

• Use negative reinforcement methods, for example blowing a horn or squirting your cat with water.

5

AGGRESSION

Feline aggression occurs most commonly between cats living in the same home. Introducing a new cat into the home is the number one cause of the problem. Sometimes cats that have lived together peacefully can suddenly become aggressive. The cause is usually territorial. If the aggression persists, separating these cats for a few days, then reintroducing them gradually usually solves the problem.

INTRODUCING A NEW CAT INTO THE HOME

• The introduction should be very gradual, and usually takes two to three weeks. Throughout this period, spend a lot of time with the cat that was there first so that he doesn't feel threatened that he is being replaced by the new cat.

• The process can be broken up into four phases. First, keep the cats in separate rooms with a closed door between them under which they can smell and hear each other. Put food and treats on each side of the door. Keep the cats apart until they are no longer concerned with each other's smell. This is called the scent recognition phase.

• Phase 2 is the face-to-face meeting. In a closed room, set two chairs facing each other, 8–10 feet apart. The cats should be in carriers or mesh pens and held on the lap,

5

When holding a cat, always support its hindquarters so that she feels safe. This is particularly important for cats that are not used to being held.

unless they are trained to wear a harness and leash. Do this twice daily for 10–15 minutes each time. Ignore the cats during these sessions and never force the situation. When the cats are no longer concerned with each other's presence, go on to the next phase.

• Phase 3 is the face-to-face meeting without leashes or carriers. Leave the cats loose in the same room, without anyone present. Always provide an escape route, for example an open door, so that neither cat feels trapped and supervise their interaction from a distance.

• Phase 4 is when the two cats are living happily together, which happens in 95 percent of cases. Wait 7–10 days before you leave them alone without any supervision.

• In cases of redirected aggression, adult cats attack people because they are mad at another cat but can't get to him. To treat this, give the cat a time-out in a quiet, dark separate room until he calms down. Try not to let him have visual contact with strange or offensive cats.

Warning

Cats that are stroked too roughly or too often may develop irritable aggression toward people. Most aggression toward people, however, is due to a cat natural predatory behavior. This can be dangerous if directed toward babies or small children (see p. 96).

Wire mesh pens allow cats to see and smell other cats in the same room, while feeling safe.

COMPLEMENTARY TREATMENTS

▢ HOMEOPATHIC REMEDIES
Skullcap and valerian tablets help to calm nervous cats.

▦ BACH FLOWER REMEDIES
Bach Rescue Remedy, 2–3 drops given with food or water 3 times daily, decreases anxiety.

5

OBSESSIVE BEHAVIOR

Obsessive behavior caused by stress can result in a cat developing an obsessive compulsive disorder (OCD). Wool-chewing and overgrooming are the most common obsessive disorders in cats. The exact causes of these disorder is unknown. Sensitive Oriental breeds such as Siamese and Burmese are often affected and may be genetically predisposed to obsessive behavior. These problems are most common in multi-cat households where cats may feel more stressed due to a lack of personal space and/or conflicts with other cats.

TYPES OF OBSESSIVE BEHAVIOR

• Wool-chewing: adult cats will sometimes start sucking or chewing wool sweaters or other materials. This occurs more in Siamese and Burmese cats than in other breeds. They usually chew wool, but if no wool items are available, will chew other materials, including upholstery, which can be costly and frustrating. Wool-chewing may occur because the cat was weaned too early. Feeding cats roughage such as vegtables and herbs gives them a chance to chew and redirects their attention away from woollen objects.

• Overgrooming (also called psychogenic alopecia): this is most common in adult Siamese and Himalayans. Signs to look for are bald, hairless areas, around the groin, hind end, and shoulders. You may see the cat licking himself obsessively, or pulling out his own fur, sometimes to the point of self-mutilation. These cats spend far more time grooming than normal cats, which spend up to 50 percent of their time grooming. Normal grooming maintains their coats and relieves stress.

WHAT YOU CAN DO

• Wool chewing is not only caused by stress, so your vet must eliminate other medical causes such as dental problems and infestation by roundworms.

• To combat wool-chewing, add fiber to your cat's diet with fresh vegetables and chopped

Give your cat lots
of extra care and
attention in potentially
stressful times.

Warning

Excessive grooming
may produce large
hairballs that get stuck
in a cat's throat or
stomach. Frequent
brushing will help to
decrease the amount
of hair your cat
swallows. If necessary,
laxatives will help to
dissolve hair already
digested.

greens, get some edible plants that your cat can chew. You can also get feline
dental chews (see p.19) from your vet, which most cats enjoy. Dabbing items
that you do not want your cat to chew with a hot pepper sauce and spraying
it with cologne may also help to discourage chewing.

• To combat overgrooming, rule out medical or physical problems first, and
then try behavior modification methods. The key to stopping unwanted
behavior is not to reinforce it, so if you catch your cat pulling at his hair,
make an unusual loud noise by blowing a whistle or clicking a clicker to
interrupt the behavior. Avoid eye contact and ignore your cat when you do
this. Then play with him vigorously to reinforce the nonlicking behavior.
Increasing the amount of daily exercise and playtime is also recommended.

• If stress is the reason for your cat's overgrooming, do whatever you can to
make your cat feel secure. Provide your cat with a separate bedroom as well
as its own litter box, food, and water bowl. Improve its diet by adding
vitamins, supplements, and fresh greens. Interactive games and playtime with
the owner help prevent boredom and loneliness. These cats require lots of love
and patience. Your vet may recommend alternative therapy products like
Rescue Remedy or, as a last resort, psychotropic drugs for stress relief.

5

HUNTING

Cats have an instinctive desire to hunt and explore. It is part of their natural predatory behavior, and usually develops by the time kittens are 7 weeks old. Extremely playful kittens may start biting your ankles, pouncing, and even attacking you. This is called playful aggression, and it is easy to resolve. Most cats grow out of it by the time they are two years old. Occasionally cats become more aggressive and start sneaking up on babies. This is called predatory aggression and can be dangerous.

Warning

If you are able to rescue a live bird or other creature from your cat, remember it will be in a state of shock, and handling should be kept to an absolute minimum. Put the creature in a dark place and seek veterinary advice. The outlook is often poor, even if the injury is not severe. This is because the bacteria injected into the body by the cat's bite are often likely to cause fatal septicemia.

WHAT YOU CAN DO

• To alleviate playful aggression, provide your cat with stimulating interactive toys that he can hunt. Toys made of fur and feathers are fun as are those that hop and move around. Give your cat lots of exercise. To keep him amused when you are out of the house, hide some treats in paper bags.

• Cats displaying signs of predatory aggression should be kept away from children and babies. Try negative reinforcements to interrupt aggressive behavior. If the cat continues to misbehave, you may need to consult a behavioral specialist.

• There is little you can do to prevent a cat from hunting animals, although neutering can reduce the hunting instinct. By offering you the catch, a cat is seeking to reinforce its bond with the family. If you find this upsetting, try fitting your cat with an elasticated collar that has a bell to warn off potential prey. The elasticity in the collar is vital so that it does not strangle the cat if it becomes caught up on a branch or some other snag.

• If you want to feed birds in your garden, hang food on thin twigs that the cat can't climb.

5

FIRST AID

To help ensure the health of your cat and your family, it's important to take a few preventative measures and use a lot of common sense. It's a good idea to have a first aid kit, to learn a few basic first aid techniques, to be familiar with poisons, and to keep them out of reach. Keep a list of emergency phone numbers on hand, including those of your vet and a 24-hour care facility. Always consult your vet before giving medicine to your cat and never give your cat any medication meant for people. If your cat develops a chronic condition, or has an ongoing health problem, keep a written record of all his medications and notes on his condition.

RAISING ORPHAN KITTENS

Raising orphan kittens is a challenge and is not always successful. About 50 percent of all kittens die within the first three days of life because they do not weigh enough. Low birth weight can be the result of several factors, such as premature birth or viral infections. Herpes virus (cat flu), leukemia, FIP, and feline distemper can all affect unborn kittens while they are still in the uterus. Vaccination of the mother helps to prevent this from occurring. Newborn kittens can also be affected by *conjunctivitis neonatorum*. This is an inflammatory condition of the conjunctiva, the white tissue lining the eyelids, which is caused by the herpes virus infection. The infection enters the eye through the eyelids before they have opened. Prompt intervention and medication prevents rupture of the cornea and permanent scarring of the eye. Most kittens will be fine.

RAISING ORPHAN KITTENS

• For the first two weeks of life, kittens can't regulate their own body temperature and need to be kept warm at 80–85°F (26-30°C).

• They need to be fed every few hours for the first week. Commercial formulas are available or you can make one by using a cup of fresh milk (half goat's milk and half cow's milk), one egg, two tablespoons of honey, and an appropriate vitamin/mineral supplement.

Warning

Orphan kittens lack the natural protection that is normally received through their mother's milk. Vaccination at 2 weeks of age is generally recommended to prevent disease.

• Use an eyedropper or a nursing bottle for feeding. Special kitten nursing bottles are available, designed to keep air bubbles out of the kitten's stomach.

• Most kittens weigh 2–4 oz at birth. They require about 2 tsp of formula per 1 oz of bodyweight per 24 hours. Divide this amount into feeds given every 3–4 hours. Warm the formula to room temperature and let the kitten nurse at his own pace.

• Later, feeding every 6–8 hours will be enough. At 3–4 weeks, when the kittens have teeth, offer small amounts of canned food mixed with milk 3–4 times daily. They should be fully weaned at 8 weeks.

SHOCK

Shock is defined as a collapse of the heart and lungs. It can be caused by a variety of life threatening situations in which a cat's blood flow and oxygen supply are impaired. Shock occurs in three phases and in the early phases is reversible. The signs in each phase are a response to a lack of blood and oxygen. Recognizing these signs, knowing what to do and when, can mean the difference between life and death.

CAUSES

• Poisoning by products toxic to cats like potpourri oils and insecticides can cause shock if inhaled or ingested.

• Blood loss caused by animal attack, anemia or being hit by a car etc.

• Chronic illness caused by bacterial or viral infection, cancer, or a systemic disease.

• Hypothermia can result from exposure to cold temperatures or can be be caused by a loss of body heat brought about by severe shock.

WHAT YOU AND YOUR VET CAN DO

• Know the symptoms for each stage of shock. In phase one, the cat's pulse and breathing rate increase and the gums may change from a light pink to a dark, reddish color. In phase two, the areas furthest from the heart such as the ear tips and tail feel cool to the touch and the rectal temperature begins to drop. In phase three, gums become a pale white color, pulse and breathing rate slow down, the cat feels cold to the touch and may lose consciousness. If the heart or lungs stop working, the cat may die.

• Immediate veterinary care is essential for any pet you suspect of being in shock. Keep your cat warm while on your way to the vet by wrapping it in a towel or blanket. If you can, phone ahead to warn the vet you are coming.

• While travelling to the vet, you may need to control any bleeding present and to give CPR if the cat's heart stops beating, so take along a friend or family member if possible. If poisoning is suspected, bring the vet as much information as possible on the substance involved.

6

DANGERS IN THE HOME

Potential dangers to cats in the home include drugs, plants, drain cleaners, suntan lotion, shoe polish, household cleaners, gardening and lawn-care supplies, car-care products, as well as insecticides and baits. Actual reports of cats getting seriously ill from eating plants are relatively rare compared to reports of poisoning from household products and drugs. Pet poisoning by household drugs is responsible for 75 percent of toxin exposure and carries a 20 percent fatality rate. One extra-strength Tylenol can kill a 7-pound cat. Signs of toxicity are usually vague and may include salivation, vomiting, and weakness.

HOUSEPLANT HAZARDS

• A lot of household plants just cause an upset stomach, but persistent or severe vomiting is a danger sign. Lilies are very toxic. Eating a few leaves from a Tiger or Easter lily can cause ulcers of the mouth and stomach. Kidney failure and a life-threatening anemia can also result. Other houseplants to avoid include azaleas, foxgloves, philodendrons, cyclamens, Jerusalem cherries, dieffenbachias, dragon trees, spiderplants, airplane plants (crassula), and caladiums.

HOLIDAY HAZARDS

• Taking a few precautions will help to ensure a safe and happy holiday season for you and your cat. Linear foreign objects such as ribbon, string, and tinsel are favorites for curious cats and kittens. Once swallowed they can cause painful intestinal problems.

• Christmas tree sap is toxic and fallen pine needles can perforate the stomach if swallowed. Secure your tree with netting or prevent your cat from having access to the room when you are not home. Holiday candles should be kept out of reach, and the fireplace should be protected by a fireguard.

• Mistletoe is one of the deadliest products for cats and dogs. The berries can upset a pet's stomach, then cause the heart to stop beating. Holly berries, on the other hand, may cause vomiting and diarrhea, but are not fatal.

6

Curious cats, love warm, cozy places like your clothes dryer. A cat that has been shut in a dryer may suffer heat stroke, shock, and even death. Keep the doors of your washer and drier shut.

POISONING

• Potpourri oils have recently become very popular as household fragrances. They contain "essential or natural" oils. A lot of people buy them but don't realize that they can be toxic. If pets accidentally ingest these oils (by licking them off their coats for example), they can cause vomiting, diarrhea, and liver damage.

• Products that contain naphthalene, such as mothballs, can be fatal if eaten. Raw sourdough contains enough ethanol to poison a pet. Homemade playdough contains high levels of salt, which is dangerous for cats with heart and/or kidney problems. Many household cleaning agents contain chemicals, which, like essential oils, are caustic. Find a nontoxic alternative. Most pets stop eating because of painful burns to the mouth. Without treatment, kidney failure and anemia can result.

Warning

Holiday plants like poinsettias, ivy, and mistletoe are potentially toxic, but seldom cause serious clinical signs if eaten. Keep them in a separate room from your cat, or place them out of your cat's reach.

6

DANGERS IN THE YARD

Cats tend to wander far afield when you let them outside, so you will not be able to supervise them as closely as if they were in the home. Even so, by appreciating the potential dangers, not only will you be able to avoid them in your yard, but you can also be alert to the problems that may crop up and react appropriately.

PLANT HAZARDS

• Certain plants are toxic. Do not let your cat eat onions, garlic, or other plants from the Lily family. Eating any part of these can be fatal. Onions, once ingested, can destroy red bood cells and result in severe anemia, which can be fatal if it is not controlled.

• When a cat's skin and hair rubs against the leaves of plants like tomatoes, strawberries, and cucumbers, it is an irritant. A skin rash and sunburn are both potential risks. If plants are eaten, blisters in the mouth can also result. Daffodil bulbs are toxic and the berries of deadly nightshade and Japanese yew are fatal.

• Tulips, iris, and hyacinth flowers as well as all kinds of mushroom are also toxic for cats.

OUTDOOR HAZARDS

• Place insect baits carefully. They smell and taste good, which attracts rodents and pets. Slug bait is a major problems for pets on the West Coast. Rat poison causes internal bleeding, which can be fatal. Certain wood preservatives, epoxy adhesives, and fungicides are also toxic.

6

If your cat is allowed to roam freely in your neighborhood, there is little you can do to monitor her safety. You can, however, make your garden a safer place for her to be.

WINTERTIME HAZARDS

Winter brings special dangers for your pet, and special precautions are necessary to protect it.

• Cats hide in or under car engines to get warm and can be seriously, if not fatally, injured. Always blow your horn and tap on the hood before starting your car in winter. Temperatures below 20°F (–7°C) are too cold for most pets to be outside very long. Hypothermia and frostbite are both risks.

• If your cat does not have access to clean, unfrozen water, she is likely to drink whatever she can find. This may include dangerous household chemicals or antifreeze. Antifreeze is particularly dangerous because its sweet smell appeals to cats. The active ingredient is ethylene glycol, which is toxic to the neurological system and kidneys. It is also present in hydraulic brake fluids and some paints and plastics. Signs of poisoning are depression, lack of coordination, vomiting, and seizure. It is essential to get the cat to the vet at once because it will be fatal if not caught within two hours of ingestion. Two teaspoons are enough to kill a cat. Agents such as denatornium benzoate, which taste bitter, are being added to antifreeze to prevent this problem.

• Keep any poison containers closed and well locked away. Clean up spills immediately and get rid of whatever you've used to mop up straight into the garbage can.

6

HIT BY CAR

A very common cause of feline emergencies is automobile accidents. The term used by vets is "HBC," meaning "hit by car." Some cats in automobile accidents are lucky enough to escape with minor wounds, bruises, or lacerations. Most cats, however, end up with broken bones and/or other internal injuries. Regardless of how a cat looks externally, if she has been hit by a car she should be examined thoroughly by a vet as soon as possible.

Warning

Approach injured animals carefully. Even your own pet can become aggressive when he is frightened and in pain. Watch for body language: cats crouched down with their ears laid back that twitch their tails may bite. If necesary, call your local animal shelter.

WHAT YOU CAN DO

• If your cat is not moving, you need to be sure that she is alive. Touch the cornea (center) of her eye. If she is alive, she should blink.

• If your cat is unconscious, treat her just as you would a person with a possible spine injury. Place her on a board so that her legs, spine and neck are straight. Next, be sure that her airway is clear so that she is able to breathe. You can gently extend her head and neck, and use a cloth to clear any secretions from her mouth.

Cats have a habit of sitting under cars and dashing out unexpectedly into the road.

At night, when on the prowl, cats can easily be blinded by oncoming headlights, and end up being hit by a car. Cats wearing a collar with a reflective strip may be more obvious to drivers.

• If the cat is bleeding, the first aid treatment is the same as that used for a person. Apply steady, direct pressure with a clean towel, a piece of gauze, or even your hand to try to stop or at least limit the blood flow. One pellet of arnica montana 30c can be placed on the tongue every 30 minutes for a total of three doses to relieve pain and decrease swelling while on the way to the vet.

• Next, be sure that your cat's airway is clear so that she can breathe. If not, use cardiopulmonary resuscitation (CPR) as a last resort. To open the airway, gently extend the head and neck, open her mouth and clear any secretions or mucus. Then, pull her tongue forward, close her mouth and place your mouth over the cat's mouth and nose and gently blow five times. To get the circulation moving, place the palm of your hands over the ribs just behind the area where the elbow meets the chest. Your other hand must be underneath her right side. Press firmly. Perform six compressions then one breath. Repeat the CPR process until you detect a strong pulse or arrive at the vet's.

• You should phone ahead and let your vet know that you are on your way. If it's an odd hour, calling ahead ensures that the clinic is actually open.

WHAT YOUR VET CAN DO

• Once at the hospital, your cat will be assessed and therapy will depend on her exact status. Cats in critical condition usually need fluids, which are given through a catheter inserted into a vein. This stablizes blood pressure and prevents shock. X rays rule out fractures and other internal injuries that may not be obvious.

6

CUTS AND WOUNDS

Cuts and wounds are not uncommon in any pet. Deep lacerations can involve arteries and veins as well as nerves and underlying muscles. Outdoor cats that are hit by cars or fight with other animals often end up with multiple wounds. Certain areas tend to bleed more than others and can make the lesion look worse than it actually is. The exact treatment required will depend on the specific lesion.

WHAT YOU AND YOUR VET CAN DO

• If a cat is bleeding, apply direct pressure to stop the flow. It is best to use gauze or a clean bandage, but anything available, including your hand, will do.

• Release the pressure after a couple of minutes. If the bleeding stops, get access to the wound. Use clippers or scissors to remove hair from the area, then take an iodine-type soap and clean the wound gently. Rinse it out again with hydrogen peroxide.

• If there is a lot of hair surrounding the wound, before you clip the hair, coat it with water-soluble K-Y jelly. The hairs will stick to the jelly and not to the wound, so will be easier to wash away. Cover the wound with gauze, tape it in place, and reassess the wound the next morning. Always give your vet a call, just to be sure.

• If the bleeding does not stop, continue applying direct pressure to the wound while on your way to the vet. For body wounds, having a 4-inch ace bandage on hand helps a lot. You can wrap the cat's entire torso using the bandage. It applies pressure, covers the wound, and usually helps to stop the bleeding.

• To help to restrain the cat, you may need to grab a handful of loose skin and hair, which is called the scruff, behind their neck and support the body with the other hand.

An Elizabethan collar helps to prevent cats from traumatizing a wound, but most cats don't like wearing them.

6

Cats always seem to have an admirable sense of balance, but because of their adventurous natures they will often injure themselves through climbing on fencing.

COMPLEMENTARY TREATMENTS

HERBAL REMEDIES

Calendula (marigold) extract is useful for flushing a wound and also promotes healing of the tissue . Use 5 drops to ½ cup of distilled water.

Calendula-hypericum ointment applied to a minor wound will promote healing. Leave the wound open.

Horsetail Grass Tea also promotes healing. Add 1 tsp to meals twice daily for 4 weeks.

HOMEOPATHIC REMEDIES

Silica 6x encourages wounds to heal. Use 1 pellet on tongue every four hours for 3–5 days

BACH FLOWER REMEDIES

Bach Rescue Remedy calms the cat down while on the way to the vet. Place 3 drops in your cat's mouth every 30 minutes.

6

BROKEN BONES

The most common cause of broken bones in cats is automobile accidents. Other causes include fights between dogs and cats, severe falls, and various bone diseases, including cancer. Sometimes you can tell if your cat has a broken leg because it is extremely swollen, or he is holding it in an unusual position. The worst cases are open wounds with visible pieces of bone sticking out, which are at high risk of infection.

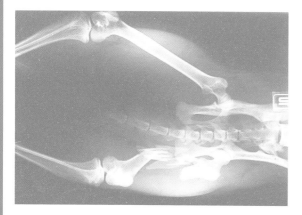

A shattered thigh bone is evident in this X ray. This bone, the femur, can be repaired in a variety of ways.

WHAT YOU AND YOUR VET CAN DO

• If you think your cat may have a broken bone, place her in a carrier or small box and take her to the animal hospital immediately. Diagnosis of a fracture is made by taking an X ray of the bones.

• If you think a leg is broken and you live a long way from a vet, you may have to make a splint. Use a couple of pieces of newspaper or a small towel. Wrap it round the fracture including the joint above and below the break and then secure it with tape. Do not attempt this unless it is strictly necessary.

• Your vet will take an X ray of the affected area, which is likely to entail anesthesia. It may be possible to set the fracture immediately.

• Limb fractures may be repaired by being encased in fiberglass or plaster casts, and by wiring, stainless steel pinning, or plating. Casts work best on fractures on the lower part of a leg. After a cast is put on, fractures are rechecked at 30-day intervals for healing. Once the fracture is mended, the cast is removed. Pins are generally left in until the fracture heals, usually in about four to eight weeks, then removed under anesthesia. Plates and screws are used to repair fractures with odd shapes, like the pelvis, or badly broken front or hind leg bones.

6

ANIMAL ATTACKS

Wildlife attacks on domestic pets are not uncommon and several diseases can be transmitted that affect both human and animal health, of which rabies is the most prevalent. If your cat is attacked you can evaluate his condition before visiting the vet by checking his rate of respiration, which should normally be 20–30 breaths per minute. If cats are scared they can pant up to 300 times per minute, but if they pant for more than a few minutes then the problem is critical. Other checks include taking his rectal temperature, normally 101–102.5°F (38.3–39°C), and his heart rate, normally 160–220 beats per minute.

Warning

In many parts of the world, snake bites represent a hazard to cats, but unless you are present when your cat is bitten, the cause of its sudden collapse will be not be obvious. Emergency veterinary treatment is absolutely essential under these circumstances. If you do see a snake, but cannot identify it, write down a description. This will make it easier for the vet to identify the snake and give the most effective treatment.

WHAT YOU AND YOUR VET CAN DO

• Cleaning wounds once or twice daily with hydrogen peroxide helps prevent infection. Some wounds heal cleanly, but abscesses (see p. 62) will develop in others.

• Abscesses usually take from 3–7 days to appear after an attack. Most need to be lanced, flushed and drained by your vet.

• A pillowcase sometimes comes in handy when transporting a frightened cat. They are porous enough for a cat to breath, and most walk in freely and feel secure.

• Cats may find toads irresistible prey because they are slow moving and easy to catch. Once in the cat's mouth, however, the toxins from the toad's skin will cause it to start foaming, forcing the cat to drop it. You will need to flush out the cat's mouth with water, if at all possible, and then contact your vet for advice.

6

FIRST AID KIT

Always keep a first aid kit handy as you never know when you might need it. You can buy one or put one together yourself. Below are the basic items that you will need.

FIRST AID KIT

• Thermometer to check your cat's body temperature. The usual rectal temperature for a cat is 101–102.5°F (38.3–39°C).

• Bandage materials, scissors, adhesive tape, triple antibiotic ointment for cuts and scrapes, and dressing for wounds.

• Artificial tears to flush eyes.

• A blanket for warmth or to use as a stretcher.

• Dishwashing liquids (with a mild grease-cutting action) can be used to bathe a cat after skin contamination to reduce exposure to insecticides and potpourri.

• Kaopectate for diarrhea. Use ½ tsp three times daily.

• Bach Flower Rescue Remedy for calming down cats (and owners) in an emergency. Arnica for calming cats with traumatic injuries. Styptic powder helps to stop bleeding (especially under claws).